Wizard of the dribble Merv Grist is a devout follower of his local Trowbridge Town (any resemblance to Athletico Whaddon is entirely coincidental). His Les Bence character first appeared in his own fanzine and was snapped up for a seven-figure transfer by leading footie mag *When Saturday Comes*.

Life at the Tip

Les Bence on the Game

Merv Grist

First published in Great Britain in 1993 by
Virgin Books
an imprint of Virgin Publishing Ltd
332 Ladbroke Grove
London W10 5AH

A catalogue record for this book is available from the British
Library

ISBN 0 86369 613 9

Illustrations by Phil Healey

Phototypeset by Intype, London
Printed and bound by
Cox & Wyman, Reading, Berks

ATHLETICO WHADDON FOOTBALL CLUB

FOUNDED 1911

FORMER NAMES Blazers Sleepibye Beds Sports and Welfare; Mitchley and Whaddon Athletic; Whaddon and Mitchley Athletic; Whaddon Athletic

CHAIRMAN Mr Kenneth Mentle OBE

MANAGER Mr Leslie Bence RAC

GROUND The Tip, Tip Lane (unclassified road), Mitchley Road

CAPACITY 750 (paying) 2,000 (non-paying)

RECORD ATTENDANCE 2,200 Mr Pastry and The Sooty Show (1963)

RECORD ATTENDANCE (ALLEGED) 200,000 v. Mitchley Borough (every year before the war)

RECORD WIN 5–0 v. Whaddon Methodist Sunday School XI (1947)

RECORD DEFEAT 13–1 v. Hexley Utd (1949); Felton (1957, 1973, 1989); Wendle Colliery Spartans (1951); Ogley (1948); Northtown FC (1977, 1987); Galvanised Steel Marwick (1966); Dagenham Girl Pipers XI (1971)

MOST GOALS IN A SEASON 672 (including training sessions)

MOST LEAGUE GOALS 31 (season 71/72)
MOST GOALS AGAINST approx. 301 (season 71/72; 75/76; 87/88; 88/89)
MOST CAPPED PLAYER none
PLAYER WITH MOST CAPPED TEETH Len Furlow (Whaddon 1968–70)
PLAYERS WITH LEAGUE/INTERNATIONAL EXPERIENCE Mike Channon (signing imminent)
LEAGUE AND CUP HONOURS see below

CRAMBE REPETITA

ATHLETICO WHADDON SUPPORTERS' CLUB NEWSLETTER

MANAGER'S WELCOME

BOTTOM OF DIVISION TWO (How they finished last season)

	P	W	D	L	F	A	PTS
Lake Town	34	10	10	14	83	56	40
Corwick Rgers	34	10	4	20	42	64	34
A. WHADDON	34	3	3	28	24	103	12

Good grief, no sooner has the final whistle blown than we here at Athletico Whaddon are gearing ourselves up ready for the hurly-burly of next season's campaign.

Our new home will be the Multivite Vegeburger/Singletons Valve Replacement League Division Three where the standard of football is remarkably high. Not, perhaps, of the calibre we experienced last season in Division Two, and admittedly falling far short of that which graced 'The Tip' during our brief spell in Division One. However, players excel and quality rises when one's team is being cheered on by four or five thousand enthusiastic fans and even the hundred plus that turn up here every week can lift a team, so, please, continue your support in the forthcoming season.

Relegation, it must be said, came hard, but of course was not a new experience here at Athletico Whaddon. After all, it was only a season ago that we were last relegated, but the spirit within the club is such that we can bounce right back, of that I am sure. Personally, I take some comfort in knowing that I in no way contributed to our exit from Division Two. When I took over, the 'Whads' were already twenty points adrift from the rest of football and while not seeing myself beyond blame entirely, my denial of any involvement in our downfall does not mean my commitment is any less than 110 per cent. I would gladly have accepted the post of manager even if I had not won it in the club raffle.

Dedication is also the byword of our chairman, Mr Ken Mentle, and once again he has no hesitation in offering me a substantial amount of promises for next season. Ken's undying devotion to this club should be applauded by players, directors and supporters alike. For, even in these difficult times, he still holds dear the thought of League football arriving at 'The Tip'. As he said to me after relegation was confirmed last season, 'League football is still only fifteen divisions away, Les.'

Athletico Whaddon 1992–1993

MULTIVITE VEGEBURGER/ SINGLETONS VALVE REPLACEMENT LEAGUE DIVISION THREE FIXTURES 1992/1993

DATE	OPPONENT	VENUE
5 Sept.	CHAMDEN CITY RESERVES	A.
12 Sept.	SCRIMLEY ARSENAL	H.
16 Sept.	HELLINGBOROUGH	A.
19 Sept.	FRAMPTON ROVERS	A.
26 Sept.	BOTHAM WANDERERS	H.
29 Sept.	SIDCOMBE	A.
3 Oct.	SPORTING HYDRA CHEMICALS	A.
6 Oct.	GOSLING CELTIC	H.
10 Oct.	CLANSFORD UNITED	A.
17 Oct.	NORTHTOWN	A.
7 Nov.	REDLAND PARK AVENUE	H.
14 Nov.	BOTHAM WANDERERS	A.
21 Nov.	FELTON	H.
5 Dec.	TWITCHIT ALBION	A.
19 Dec.	DORNING TOWN	H.
26 Dec.	LEECH TOWN	A.
16 Jan.	SIDCOMBE	H.
26 Jan.	SCRIMLEY ARSENAL	A.
30 Jan.	CHAMDEN CITY RESERVES	H.
6 Feb.	FRAMPTON ROVERS	H.
20 Feb.	SPORTING HYDRA CHEMICALS	H.
23 Feb.	ALBORNE	A.

27 Feb.	NORTHTOWN	H.
6 Mar.	CLANSFORD UNITED	H.
13 Mar.	TWITCHIT ALBION	H.
20 Mar.	DORNING TOWN	A.
23 Mar.	FELTON	A.
3 Apr.	ALBORNE	H.
13 Apr.	REDLAND PARK AVENUE	A.
17 Apr.	LEECH TOWN	H.
24 Apr.	GOSLING CELTIC	A.
1 May	HELLINGBOROUGH	H.

LES IN CONFIDENCE

MONDAY, 7th SEPTEMBER
LABOUR DAY (CANADA)

Dear God, I must give up drink.

It was drink that got me into this mess. That and the club raffle. If I had kept my wits and remained coherent I would probably have realised the manager's job was third prize. If I had been sober I would never have bloody claimed it! Still, at least I put my bottle where my mouth is, not like those whingeing sods at 'The Tip'.

It dawned on me last season, as we took a first-minute lead over Carlton Town West Saxons, that perhaps it was Fate that plucked pink, 544, from the hat. At that moment of jubilation I realised that my own philosophy on life and that of football management go hand in foot. Surely it cannot be long before the Football League discovers what is festering in the Multivite Vegeburger/ Singletons Valve Replacement League sewer. Should the FA come calling I would take any managerial post offered, even Coventry City.

But what have I got? Athletico Whaddon. A bunch of boozed up neverbeens who would struggle to get a draw against half a box of Subbuteo. I might fool the fans, but the best I can hope for this season must be second from bottom and the third preliminary round of the FA Cup. OK, we kicked off with a win at Chamden, but they only had five men and most of those looked old enough to remember Bolton Wanderers on *Match of the Day*. As for my shower, only Marley looks like he might have talent, he seems capable of scoring goals with either his left or his right buttock.

WEDNESDAY, 9th SEPTEMBER

Two days to go before the first home game of the season. Programme notes and a bottle of Bells to get through.

Mentle has suggested I do a flattering team profile, but fiction was never my strong point. How the hell does he expect me to keep a straight pen? Look at Micky Deere, he's a complete waste of space. He's as short-sighted as a bat with its eyes shut, but with his goggles on he is a lousy attacker and without them a serious threat to our defence! Phil Meek is no improvement. God knows what Pybus saw in him, because if you could buy skill Meek would be bankrupt and still a crap player. Likewise his other 'great' find, Colin Webley. Do me a favour, Webley couldn't even pass a mug of tea across the counter last season, let alone pass a ball.

Thankfully, that win backed up my insistence that we re-sign Trevor Proby. It had been tough going, but Proby was grateful enough to knock a century off the £500 I owe him. Ken Mentle argued that Trevor needed psychiatric treatment more than another chance in an Athletico shirt. Well, I am no medical man, but that is an understatement.

I must look out Chester's Junior Trustees Savings Account Book. Surely, if I beg nicely, he will lend his old dad four hundred quid.

ATHLETICO ·WHADDON

M/SV. DIVISION 3

TODAY
·V·
SCRIMLEY ARSENAL

£1

* OFFICIAL PROGRAMME *

MANAGER'S NOTES

12th September '92

P	W	D	L	F	A	PTS
1	1	0	0	2	1	3

Well, here we go into our first home game of the new season with a 100 per cent record so far in Division Three. Our surprise away win at Chamden City Reserves last Saturday means that Athletico Whaddon has its first unbeaten run in nineteen seasons. WELL DONE, LADS!

This was a thoroughly inspired performance by the team, for which I must take all the credit. It was unfortunate for spectators that Chamden were unable to raise a full side but this should not detract from our victory, although all praise to the five Chamden lads for holding our rampant attack to a slender 2–1.

The only sad note of the afternoon was the heart attack suffered by our chairman, Ken Mentle, just after the final whistle. I am pleased to report that Ken's attack was not major and that he is well on the way to recovery. I am sure we all wish him the best of luck. GET WELL SOON, SON.

*　　　*　　　*　　　*　　　*　　　*　　　*

Today sees the debut of a number of new and not so new summer signings. Royston Marley comes to us from Ross Chicken Ltd. The Jamaican-born centre-forward (37) spent much of last season at Spurs where he watched every home game.

Other new faces this season: Jason Pratt is a 15-year-old 'find' by club coach Reg Pybus. Jason hails from St Dodimeads Comprehensive School whose Under-14 side held us to a very creditable 0–0 draw two seasons ago in the County Knock-Out Shield. He is a talented lad who shows great respect for his elders and will play in any position I tell him to. Colin Webley (36) is another newcomer as far as playing is concerned, although many of you will know him as the chap who did sterling work in the tea hut last season. Colin, a born darts player, was so keen to play for the 'Whads' that he paid his own signing-on fee (£56), and has also agreed to wash the team strip every week. Colin will play at left back and is club captain for the season. We also welcome back a former club captain, Trevor 'Killer' Proby (52) after a four-year suspension. Trevor, experienced in attack and abuse to officials, will prove invaluable. Many supporters, I know, feel uneasy that Proby is returning and are dismayed that we have not seen the last of what the *Whaddon and Mitchley Argus* called 'The Headcase Half Back'.

Let me put forward the case for re-signing Proby. Despite a disciplinary record that reflects his competitive nature, Trevor has a lot of skill and in many ways is a credit to the side. Football is a hard game for hard men. There is no room for a player with kid gloves on his feet, no room for sentiment, only sediment out there on the park. When you are on rung 356 of soccer's hierarchical ladder you have to fight all the way. When Trevor Proby has the ball between his legs he is a very big cog in the 'Whads' wheel. Non-League football is not about offside traps and delicate passing skills, it is about clogging and war. Wars are won by tanks not soft tackles. Remember that.

The rest of this season's squad has a lot of old faces in it. Many of these stalwarts could, I am sure, play at a higher level of football and we are lucky that their devotion to the club and my management skills keep them here. Micky Deere (49), one of our longest serving players, has proved time and again how badly we need an experienced defender. This season Micky will be sporting some new lenses, over four inches thick, in his match-day bi-focals. Young goalie, John Slack (38), has recovered from a dislocated shoulder and broken nose he sustained during a pre-season tactical discussion with Trevor Proby and is eager to take up that vital position between the posts once again. At 53 most players would have only dusty memories of their days in combat, but Dave Doyle, the 'Cliff Richard of football', still turns out every season for his beloved Whaddon. It is only natural that his pace has slowed and perhaps that gazelle-like mind, which was such an influence on the young George Best, may have dulled, but if I had eleven Dave Doyles in my side then we would make the *Guinness Book Of Records* and cause referees and opponents utter confusion. Confused is a word I would use to describe Darren Twink's (24) dazzling ball skills. 'Twinky' is now in his second season with us after failing to make his mark in Sunday football. Here at Whaddon I have allowed his talent to blossom and I would not be surprised to see the League big boys sniffing after him before Christmas, and Darren to be a regular in Barnet reserves by the end of the season. Despite openly admitting to owning the entire recorded works of Chicory Tip, Terry Wade (44) does not let his eccentricities interfere with his on-field performance; despite his refusal to turn out on Eurovision Song Contest ay. Last season, remember, he headed three glorious goals before the FA banned his innovative platform football boots. Angus 'Jock' McDougall (56) is currently the only Polish player on Athletico's books. Ever since he was a young lad, 'Jock' has harboured ambitions of playing professional soccer. Unfortunately, he has never made the grade and after knocking on the door of inter-pub midweek leagues without success, has at last found his niche at Athletico where this season he will team up with YTS trainees Adie Smith and Phil Meek. Finally, Steve Gillery is with us again. Signed two seasons ago from Dunwick Pressed Steel Reserves where he was unable to sustain a second team place, he has found his perfect football niche here at Whaddon.

*　　　*　　　*　　　*　　　*　　　*　　　*

As no doubt the teams are ready to take the field, it only remains for me to extend a warm welcome to the directors, players and boisterous supporters of Scrimley Arsenal and wish you all an enjoyable afternoon.

SPOTLIGHT ON ATHLETICO
WHADDON 1911–1940

It was the formation of the Mid-Counties Combination League, now the Alaap Curry Mix Intermediate, that took Athletico Whaddon forerunners Blazers Sleepibye Beds Sports and Welfare FC from a works eleven to footballing representatives for the borough of Mitchley and Whaddon.

'The Beds' were formed in 1911 by local manufacturer, sportsman and historian, the eccentric P. W. Blazer. It was he who walked from Bristol to London via Glasgow and Edinburgh in papyrus sandals to prove his theory that all Roman roads turned right. Blazer offered his workforce a piece of waste ground behind the mattress shed for a pitch and it soon became affectionately known as the 'Football Ground'. Owing to an archaic local by-law, which forbade the wearing of shorts in an industrial building at weekends, the changing rooms were three miles away at the Duck and Forceps public house.

The bed magnate took charge of the team himself and could often be seen running the touchline in his pith helmet, armed with an old shotgun to encourage the lads. Leg wounds were common among players in those early days and contributed to the team's poor performances. Between 1912 and 1930 their most successful period was 1914–18 when all football was suspended because of the First World War.

By 1926, the stuffing had been knocked out of the mattress business and the factory closed. Mr Blazer also died that year and as a mark of respect and lack of interest the club folded, only to re-appear in 1931, widening their appeal by becoming Mitchley and Whaddon Athletic. However, after a lively inaugural meeting at the Duck and Forceps, punches were thrown, beer spilt and the club emerged as Whaddon and Mitchley Athletic. Then, just before the club's debut v. Cromley Royal Artillery (1931) Ltd, fighting broke out in the dressing room and the Mitchley contingent in the crowd were surprised to discover the team was five players short and called Whaddon Athletic. With five volunteers from the 400-plus crowd, a 12–1 defeat at the hands of the soldiers was not a bad start.

The following week, an application was made to the county Sunday League by the breakaway quintet and friends as the rival Mitchley Borough. Over the years a niggling rivalry has been much in evidence between the two clubs, although Whaddon have progressed to a much higher standard of football. Mitchley, on the other hand, have deservedly spent sixty-odd years rotting in the wastelands of Sunday soccer, their only consolation being that they have won all twenty-six encounters between the two clubs since 1932.

Local grocer, Fred Plumb, became the first Athletic manager in 1932 by winning the position in a raffle, thereby setting a tradition which has continued to this day. Fred, a man of immense charm and cunning, was the man who first suggested looking beyond the lounge bar of the Duck and Forceps for potential players. Up until then, the only qualifications needed to secure a place in the team were an abnormal capacity for Nettles Agricultural Sherry, a willingness to buy a round whenever invited, an abhorrence of physical exercise and a pair of knee-length shorts. It was Fred who signed and elected Duck and Forceps landlord Bill Dodd as club captain. Despite the fact that Bill was in his mid-fifties and had a chronic heart condition, which meant he could only play for a maximum of five minutes a match, it was a good move on Fred's part as the pub owned the cricket pitch at the rear and naturally, as captain, Bill felt obliged to hand it over to the club, and so 'The Tip' was born. By the end of the 32/33 season, the club was well placed to progress from friendlies to Junior

League soccer. The opportunity arose in the close season when the FA decided to form the Mid-Counties Combination.

Whaddon saw their acceptance into the Combination as the first tentative step towards professional League football, and work was undertaken over the next five years on building and improving basic facilities at 'The Tip'. We should perhaps remember that, before the advent of television, the five-day week and DIY superstores, crowds, even for the smallest clubs, often exceeded 3,000 and for an important derby match during the 1930s Whaddon could easily pull in 120,000 fans according to some of the club's more senior supporters.

The old cricket pavilion was demolished and then cobbled back together as a grandstand able to accommodate up to fifty spectators. Ex-GWR rolling stock was soldered together, the sides removed and transformed into the popular 'Bog Hole' where today long-time supporters huddle. On the field, however, progress proved slow and fourteenth (out of sixteen) during the 35/36 season was our most notable achievement. Bill Dodd's retirement saw Cyril Proby take over the captaincy and Plumb began the job of squad rebuilding. Some of the names he enlisted will no doubt bring back fond memories for older supporters – names like Bert Fudge, 'Shin Hack' Hodges and, of course, the (then) young Kenny Mentle.

Ken's skill as a player was evident from the start. Here was a footballer the like of which the Whaddon faithful had never witnessed before. Here was a player who had clean kit for every match, who actually trained at home and, more importantly, scored goals where it mattered – between the posts.

The following two seasons saw a steady improvement in team performance, consolidating their fourteenth position from the previous season and finishing a creditable ninth (out of ten) in 36/37.

Once again, the league structure was to change, and the formation of a semi-professional super-league of five divisions was announced. Heading the new Mid-Counties

16

South-West League (Northern Division) was to be a Premier Division to which all Combination clubs were invited to apply. The FA took a unique decision here, declaring that clubs would be elected alphabetically to the five divisions. Fred Plumb now pulled a masterstroke. On the day of application he convened an extraordinary board meeting and, within minutes, announced that Whaddon Athletic was now known as Athletico Whaddon, thus ensuring Premier rather than Fifth Division football.

As the 1938/39 season began, an off-the-field crisis occurred. The club cashbox containing £3 2s 8d, two Co-op milk tokens and a First World War medal went missing. It was later traced by police to the locker of club skipper Cyril Proby. With 92 other offences taken into consideration, including arson, blackmail, three sendings-off and a professional foul, Proby was sent down and dismissed by the club. Ironically, almost fifty years later, his son Trevor, also a club captain, secured an even longer stretch at Her Majesty's pleasure.

Under the new captaincy of Ken Mentle, the club decided not to go all out for the title but simply to consolidate their Premier Division status. The idea was certainly sensible as the club gained valuable experience, finished bottom, and were relegated to Division One.

However, if Athletico had hopes of a brief stay away from the Premier they were to be disappointed. By 1940 Nazi Germany, the Wimbledon of world politics, had started up a completely different ball game.

LES IN CONFIDENCE

SATURDAY, 26th SEPTEMBER

I have just returned from today's match dazed and confused. How the hell my pack of jokers has managed two wins out of two is a complete mystery. I told them in the club bar that it was all down to my carefully structured pre-season training programme, but after last season's relegation I haven't been near the ground since April! Actually, I am trying a new strategy. Before both last week's Chamden game and this afternoon's, I fell to my knees and uttered the following words, 'Oh God, please, please, please let us win today. I promise on my old mother's teeth that I will never drink or take Bobby Charlton's name in vain again. Thank you, God, thank you.' Well, it seems to work.

I thought the victory over Chamden would put an end to the ridicule and abuse the Whaddon 'rotweillers' have subjected me to, but no chance. Today's game I thought would be a good opportunity to rub the buggers' noses in it. I got to the ground early and strung up a 'Well done Les' banner over the turnstile, but in less than ten minutes Micky Deere had wiped his nose on one end and cleaned last week's mud off his boots with the other. Still, I was determined to cash in on my success and maintain a high profile at the ground. I greeted fans on their arrival with a shake of the hand and an offer to autograph their match programmes at a reasonable £1.50 a time. Of course, I knew my success would cause resentment. I have been a manager long enough to know the fans only look on me as a punch bag, constantly on the end of the verbal one-two. My new fedora and Hamlet cigar accessories, more fitting to a winning manager than my old tartan pom-pom cap and ounce of Old Holborn, made me unrecognisable to most of the supporters and the nearest I received to a compliment came from a director who suggested I 'stick a faggot up my backside and clear off'. Well, the way things are going this season I could well be clearing off. I have it on good authority from a cousin in Stockport, who has a drinking buddy who knows the car park attendant at Altrincham, that my name has already been linked with a managerial post at both Rotherham and Manchester United. Let me tell you, when those dubbin-lickers at Whaddon go on their knees and beg me to bring my United first team squad to 'The Tip' to put a few quid in their ailing coffers, I shall take great delight in treading on Ken Mentle's fingers, provided he survives last week's heart attack, and raising two toes in a defiant 'get lost' gesture.

I am the first person to admit that success is not that frequent at Athletico and on those rare occasions when it comes we are always left with a nasty aftertaste to spoil it. That aftertaste is Trevor Proby. The Lord knows I did my best. As soon as I heard that Mr Hudd would be linesman today I begged the League to appoint a different official. It was Hudd, five seasons ago, who waved his flag furiously at referee Hobbs when, unsighted, he failed to spot Proby forcing his shinpad down the throat of Mossborough Sandinista's Keith Driscoll until alerted by the enthusiastic linesman.

I have known Trevor for many years and he is a mass of seething hate before breakfast most days, so I could smell the revenge in him even above 'Jock' McDougall's armpits before we left the changing room this afternoon. It came as no surprise when he was sent off for a vicious headbutt to the hapless Hudd.

After the match Trevor and I had a heated argument

over what will, undoubtedly, be another suspension. I got nowhere, of course, because in an argument Trevor can be very persuasive.

REMEMBER: HAVE A FURTHER X-RAY ON THE MIDDLE FINGERS OF MY LEFT HAND ON TUESDAY.

ATHLETICO WHADDON

M/SV. DIVISION 3.

TODAY
· V ·
BOTHAM WANDERERS

£1

✱ OFFICIAL PROGRAMME ✱

	P	W	D	L	PTS
GOSLING CELTIC	4	3	1	0	10
ATH. WHADDON	4	3	1	0	10
NORTHTOWN	4	3	0	1	9
ALBORNE	4	3	0	1	9
CLANSFORD UTD	4	2	2	0	8
REDLAND PARK AVENUE	4	2	1	1	7
SCRIMLEY ARSENAL	4	2	0	2	6
FELTON	4	2	0	2	6
DORNING TOWN	4	1	2	1	5
FRAMPTON ROVERS	4	1	2	1	5
HELLINGBOROUGH	4	1	1	2	4
LEECH TOWN	4	1	1	2	4
CHAMDEN CITY RESERVES	4	0	2	2	2
SIDCOMBE	4	0	2	2	2
SPORTING HYDRA CHEMICALS	4	0	2	2	2
TWITCHIT ALBION	4	0	2	2	2
BOTHAM WDRS	4	0	0	4	0

MANAGER'S NOTES

26th September '92
WE DO NOT REFUND ENTRANCE MONEY.

May I take this opportunity to say how sickened I was by the small group of supporters hounding the ticket kiosk for their money back, after Monday night's County Shield match against Whaddon YMCA.

Such is the standard of junior sides in this competition that the game appeared to be no more than a formality for us, so our 4–1 defeat came as a complete surprise. What supporters seem to overlook is that football is a game of two sides – one side has to lose otherwise it is a draw. Whaddon YMCA were a completely unknown quantity. At kick-off their team, like the match programme, was a blank sheet. After witnessing their performance I am not sure those supporters who thought they spotted four or five Danish internationals in the side (probably on a hiking tour of Britain), were mistaken. If this was indeed the case, then I think we played exceptionally well.

I am not offering excuses, but up against such class it was unfortunate that we could not field a side at full strength. Royston Marley's decision to work a permanent nightshift means he is now unavailable for anything but a three o'clock kick-off. We were also without that rock in defence, Trevor Proby. 'Killer', as you probably know, is currently under suspension following the harmless headbutting of a linesman during the Scrimley Arsenal game, and this has left a big hole in Mr Hudd's forehead, not to mention our defence.

Anyway, defeat in the County Shield may be for the best because, let's not be hasty, but after just four games we look like having Division Three wrapped up. You may recall we overcame a spirited Chamden side in the opening fixture, then handed out a 1–0 demolition to Scrimley Arsenal (Marley 58 mins), slaughtered Hellingborough on their own ground 2–1 (three own goals by 'Borough's one-eyed left back, Hazlett), then massacred Frampton Rovers in last Saturday's impressive 1–1 draw. Has there even been a better start to the season? How about a standing ovation for the team when they take the field this afternoon?

COMEONYOUWHADS!

*   *   *   *   *   *   *

One man who, if possible, would be leading the cheering today is, of course, our chairman, Mr Ken Mentle. Unfortunately Ken's recovery has suffered a setback after seeing us still in the title race with only fourteen-sixteenths of the season remaining. In his absence, fellow director Mr Pahdra Singh, well known proprietor of the 8-Day Superette and Pahdra's Palace take-away, has taken over the day-to-day business of chairman. Mr Singh is young, enthusiastic and full of far-reaching ideas for this club. Already he has called an extra-ordinary meeting of directors and supporters to discuss his radical new proposals.

*   *   *   *   *   *   *

Our visitors today, Botham Wanderers, are without a win so far this season and may possibly face liquidation before its end. Like our own, Botham's finances are a little under the weather. However, Wanderers are true amateurs on the field and will no doubt battle until they give up, so let's hope Athletico can keep up the good work and send them home with three lost points and the Samaritans' telephone number.

*   *   *   *   *   *   *

Today's match ball has been sponsored by the Black Sheep Wool Shop, Mitchley High Street. It will be a new experience for both Wanderers and ourselves to play with a knitted football.

YOUR LINE TO LES

Dear Les,

During our last home match of last season, I thought the team played exceedingly well all things considered. There was a lot of passing, running about and kicking which I found encouraging for this season.

However, my enjoyment in witnessing this rejuvenated Athletico is spoilt by the fact that Terry Wade has so far persisted in wearing white shorts whilst the rest of his team mates wear the customary black. Not only do I find this displeasing on the eye but I feel it contributed significantly to our eventual relegation.

Were the odd shorts some sort of tactical move, Les?

Yours, J.H.

J.H.

How observant of you to spot that Terry Wade's shorts were a different colour and to suspect this was a tactical ploy. Of course it was.

If you cast your mind back to the 1966 World Cup, you may recall that Pak Doo Ik, the North Korean forward, also wore odd shorts and he went on to score the winner against Italy, so I thought it was worth a try.

Yours in charge,
Les Bence

Dear Mr Bence,

I have been a supporter of this club since before the war, so I know what I am talking about.

Honestly, Les, this team is the biggest load of rubbish we

have had here since I've been a supporter and I started before the war, so I know what I am talking about.

No offence, Les,

Mr G.B.

(Whaddon Light Infantry, retired)

G.B.

How nice to receive a letter so full of constructive criticism. Such an in-depth analysis of last season's loss of form obviously gives me food for thought and deserves a similarly constructive reply. Thank you for writing.

Les Bence

NOTE TO PRINTERS – PLEASE MAKE SURE THE ONE BELOW IS REMOVED! ! – LB

Dear Les,

The photographs you asked for have arrived from Amsterdam and are awaiting collection. I shall be at the back of the newsagents after midnight on Sunday. If you do not arrive I will leave the pics in the dustbin.

These are pretty hot stuff so it is £80 I am afraid. Leave the money in the third bottle of embrocation from the left.

Ted

Dear Ted,

Please do not send my personal mail addressed to the football club.

SPOTLIGHT ON ATHLETICO WHADDON 1940–1950

When war came, hostilities ended and the League disbanded for the duration.

This proved to be a frustrating time for the 'Whads', as, although fellow League clubs were losing players left, right and centre-half to the war effort, Athletico had no one fit to fight. Even dynamic centre-forward Kenny Mentle was found to be flat-footed and short-sighted. Ironically, during the war years, the pitch was in better condition than it had ever been, as it was given over to the growing of carrots and potatoes.

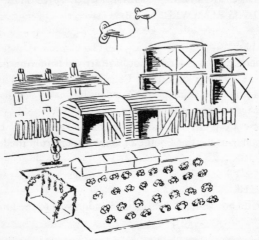

The Tip during wartime, by kind permission of Mrs Ethel Plumb

In 1943, practically the entire team relegated during 39/40 got back together during 'Buy a Spitfire' week to play a fund-raising match against a local Women's Land Army XI.

The match revealed the Athletico lads had lost none of their flair and inadequacies for the game as they narrowly went down to a 7–2 defeat. At the end of 1944 the goal posts once again replaced bean poles and 'The Tip' staged its own international fixture when a combined German and Italian team from the nearby POW camp took on the 'Whads', who for this match played under the name of England. They were awarded international caps, beautifully knitted by Mrs Ethel Plumb and presented by Lord Mitchley before the kick-off. The match was a hard-fought contest and after much cheating on their part, the prisoners ran out 3–0 victors with a doubtful hat-trick by Rudolph Hess. Justice was rightly done, however, when they lost the war and were again humiliated at Wembley in 1966.

Owing to a bizarre mix-up between a Japanese morse operator in the South China Sea, and new early closing times at Whaddon Post Office, when football finally got back to normal in 1946, Athletico, now fielding eleven internationals, found themselves in the Mid-Counties Combination instead of the higher Mid-Counties South-West League (Northern Division).

This was not the only blow to the club. The 46/47 season saw the forced retirement of Ken Mentle after he was struck on the knee by a lettuce thrown from a nearby allotment. On giving up as a player, Ken was a natural choice for chairman and, as he did at the end of every subsequent season, promised sweeping changes and League football by 1992.

First to go was manager Fred Plumb. By 1947, Fred was a broken man addicted to alcohol and the treble chance. His downfall was brought about by a lengthy court case in which he was wrongly accused of harbouring three war criminals (former POWs) in the Whaddon forward line.

The new man in charge was former goalkeeper, Walter 'Wally' Smott. Wally was awarded the job for his bravery in receiving extensive brain surgery after years of concussing himself on the crossbar. However, despite brain cells having been grafted from his backside, Walter staved off relegation and 1950 was heralded, by players and supporters alike, as the dawning of a new decade.

LES IN CONFIDENCE

WEDNESDAY, 23rd SEPTEMBER

It is nearly two weeks since I last touched a drink and we are still undefeated in the League. The bottle was in my hand, though, after that YMCA debacle. When that final whistle went I just wanted to throw up in the sponge bag. They were nothing more than a lousy bunch of down and outs, students (same thing in my book), and back-packing evangelists with acne. Most of them had to be introduced to one another by the referee yet they still stuffed four past us.

Luckily, my after-match tantrum in the dressing room certainly shook up my rabble and got a good performance against Frampton. They might be a conglomerate of poseurs, ex-Leaguers and Mike Channon wannabees, but they are also the best club in the division. I have cried off training tonight. My breathing is still suffering difficulties thanks to the custard slice that bastard Proby thrust up my nostrils. I persuaded Chester to cash in his Trustees account after agreeing to pay five quid for the taxi to take him to the bank. He had £2.10 in his account. Trevor was not happy.

Old mother Mentle phoned earlier to say hubbie Ken has calculated our current league position and suffered a relapse. This time it looks serious and if he is forced to resign then my own position could be in jeopardy. Ken Mentle is my only support on the board. This is hardly surprising I suppose as he recognised my managerial potential from the start. On my first day in the job he took me into the director's Portakabin, put his arm around me and, showing me the empty trophy case,

said 'Your job, Les, is to fill that cabinet before I die.'
No chance, Ken.

Just a couple of months out for Mentle would be enough for Pahdra Singh to cause havoc. It is an open secret that he and Reg Pybus are bosom pals. How else could Pybus afford to dine out at Pahdra's take-away and gain exclusive use of his portable telephone on Saturday afternoons to call the Multivite Vegeburger/ Singletons Valve hotline? I have also noticed their peculiar handshake and the strange, but identical, way in which they fold their match programmes 42 times. It seems pretty obvious they both attend the same origami evening class.

ATHLETICO WHADDON

M/SV. DIVISION 3

TODAY

·V·

GOSLING CELTIC

£1

* OFFICIAL PROGRAMME *

	P	W	D	L	PTS
GOSLING CELTIC	8	5	2	1	17
REDLAND PARK AVENUE	8	4	3	1	15
CLANSFORD UTD	8	4	3	1	15
FRAMPTON ROVERS	8	4	2	2	14
HELLINGBOROUGH	8	4	1	3	13
ALBORNE	8	4	1	3	13
ATH. WHADDON	8	4	1	3	13
NORTHTOWN	8	3	3	2	12
FELTON	8	4	0	4	12
SCRIMLEY ARSENAL	8	3	2	3	11
SPORTING HYDRA CHEMICALS	8	2	3	3	9
TWITCHIT ALBION	8	2	3	3	9
DORNING TOWN	8	1	4	3	7
LEECH TOWN	8	1	4	3	7
CHAMDEN CITY RESERVES	8	1	3	4	6
SIDCOMBE	8	1	3	4	6
BOTHAM WDRS	8	1	1	6	4

MANAGER'S NOTES

6th October '92

I have received a number of dog faeces through my letterbox this week from some of our more fanatical 'supporters' after our defeats against Botham and at Sidcombe last Tuesday evening. Well, I hope they eat their post after our 1–0 thrashing of Sporting Hydra Chemicals.

Rarely have I seen the 'Whads' play with such composure, flair and skill. Stuffing the 'Hydracals' will be one of my most cherished memories when I look back on my spell as manager of Athletico Whaddon. As for those defeats at the hands of Botham and Sidcombe I would rate both, in footballing terms, as nightmares. To allow Botham Wanderers, who at the time were without a win, to take a four-goal lead was asking for trouble. I had expected them at that stage to do the decent thing and wait for us to catch up but, smelling their first blood of the season, they continued in much the same fashion and eventually ran out 7–0 victors.

I can offer little in the way of explanation for our disappointing display, although the failure of goalkeeper John Slack to turn up severely crippled the team. I was forced to put Micky Deere between the posts and the referee's insistence that he remove his bi-focals meant he was two fathoms below useless. Obviously, such a run of bad luck, after the fabulous start to the season, jolted the lads and their performance at Sidcombe must have warmed the hearts of those seven supporters who travelled to the game. There can be no doubt that we benefited from having 'Slacky' back in goal. I felt he had a particularly fine game and brought off some devastating rugby tackles on the Sidcombe forwards. It was, however, unfortunate that he could not save the resultant penalties which gave Sidcombe an undeserved 3–0 win.

*   *   *   *   *   *   *

Today we take on the League leaders, Gosling Celtic, and will be out to prove our Top Ten position is no fluke. Our team will be as near full strength as possible, although once again injuries are beginning to dog us. Out today are Micky Deere (headache), Royston Marley (badly pecked knees) and Steve Gillery (shopping). With no money to invest in new players and a squad of only thirteen, team selection is a constant problem. Today is a good case in point as both myself (21) and coach Reg Pybus (48–66?) may be called upon to play, along with a guest supporter should one step forward.

*   *   *   *   *   *   *

The need for cash has never been more urgent. Only this week, our shower and changing room have been declared a disaster area by the council. This follows the near drowning of a Public Health official. After ninety bruising minutes in the mire that is 'The Tip', the last thing we or our opponents will want on a fridge-like February Saturday, is a three-mile walk to the local Duck and Forceps' washroom, caked in mud and soggy shorts smelling as evil as a gypsy's knickers. Not only are we desperate to acquire funds for new dressing room facilities but an unfortunate accident with the club van, by person(s) unknown, has removed the tea hut. After many years in its free-standing position it now finds itself neatly stacked against the side of the grandstand. The club needs an immediate cash injection of £8,000. I am pleased to announce, therefore, that acting chairman, Mr Pahdra Singh, has secured a sponsorship deal with local funeral directors, Lonsdale and Pugh. Through this lucrative arrangement the club will receive £500 over the next ten years and the donation of a new team strip, on show for the first time today. Purple satin shorts, royal blue shirts and black socks will give us an impressive appearance and put the fear of death in opponents. In honour of our new partnership with Messrs Lonsdale and Pugh, the team will, from today, be adopting a new nickname, THE STIFFS.

SPOTLIGHT ON ATHLETICO
WHADDON 1951–1969

Tom Finney, Stanley Matthews, Nat Lofthouse, Harry Lauder. How is that for a line up?

Stan Reynolds, Harry Little, Carl Einstien and Fred Grummidge may not have the same ring about them but between 1950 and 1960 these were the names on the footballing tongues of Whaddon.

Carl Einstien – the ex-POW who sold the 'Whaddon and Mitchley Sporting Mauve' outside 'The Tip' as you left the match.

Harry Little – the turnstile operator who would let you in for a penny or five Capstan Full Strength.

Fred Grummidge – the lovable old groundsman who grew dahlias along the touchline, and upon his death had his still red-hot ashes scattered across 'The Tip' and in so doing burnt down the dressing room.

Finally, the unforgettable Stan Reynolds, a player who so loved scoring goals that he would attempt to do so in whichever net was nearest. A dull 0–0 defence-dominated, end-of-season clash could at any moment come alive with Stan on the field. So obsessive was his craving for goals he could put us one up or one down at any minute!

Crowds during the decade declined steadily. As with many non-League clubs, Athletico had to compete with more illustrious neighbours – Spurs, Liverpool, Plymouth and Celtic. All were within a 500-mile radius of Whaddon, and many misguided soccer fans preferred travelling to those grounds rather than succumb to the semi-pro subtleties on show at 'The Tip'.

Wally Smott's mediocrity raised him above many of the managers who guided the club over the years, but Athletico reserved a bottom six position from 1951 to 1955 and Ken Mentle's dream of League football became a nightmare.

During a heated board meeting in June 1955, Wally announced he was 'Going outside for a fag. I might be some time.'

Three narrow and thoroughly encouraging defeats (1–0, 5–0, 9–0) kicked off the 55/56 season and raffle winner Sid Beamish found himself at the helm. It was revealed many years later that Sid had not actually bought the winning ticket but had found it mysteriously floating in his half-time Bovril.

What could have proved a disastrous appointment did, and Athletico were only saved from oblivion by the inspired choice of Reg Pybus as coach. Reg was already a well respected backroom boy and came to the club from high-flying Walborough Solid Fuel Albion. Why he decided to drop

Coach Reg Pybus in 1957

three divisions and stay with the club until his first dismissal in 1987, remains shrouded in slipped fivers. Scurrilous newspaper allegations over the years have hinted at blackmail, involving an unsavoury incident in the Walborough shower, forged Sheffield Wednesday rosettes and a second-hand Ford Popular Reg sold to Ken Mentle in 1954.

Whatever his reasons for staying, Reg certainly knew his football and it was he who turned a team of no-hopers into one capable of sustaining a bottom six position for the rest of the decade. By the end of the 59/60 campaign, a new optimism had arrived. Beamish was slowly grasping his new-found trade and, with Pybus at his side, players and supporters saw the coming season as the dawning of a new age.

The Swinging Sixties swung into action with a 4–1 defeat on Boxing Day and the sacking of Sid Beamish just before Redland Park Avenue's third goal.

The quart bottle of Nettles scheduled for first prize in the raffle was replaced by the top job and the winning ticket, always known on these occasions as 'Ken's shilling', went to Norvm Homstat. Unlike his predecessors, Norvm had managerial experience, having formerly held the reins at Railway Sidings Malmo. Obviously, his appointment was a fix but the Homstat-Pybus partnership was seen as a surefire recipe for success.

Homstat's grasp of football management was considerable, his grasp of English nil. Not only that, but he refused to leave Sweden and would commute by Volvo, North Sea Ferry and British Rail.

With the world's transport systems not prepared to align themselves with Athletico training sessions or match kick-offs, Homstat was sometimes absent for weeks on end, giving team talks with the aid of an interpreter over the telephone, or he would be a lone, pathetic figure, sat in the dug-out on a wet Monday morning urging on thin air.

Perhaps it was the need for stability to offset the 'Whads'

sterility but, remarkably, Homstat remained with the club until 1968. He refused to compromise in any way and, throughout his long association with the club, only mastered two words in English, both of which he frequently practised on referees. After numerous bookings he was banned from the touchline, banned from the grandstand the following season and, in his last season with the club, directed play, in Swedish, from the car park with the aid of a megaphone.

His astronomical travelling expenses all but bankrupted the club, and his non-appearance at over half the games sapped team morale. Further financial difficulties arose when he signed Swedish quadruplets Hans, Benny, Bjorn and Agnetha Larsson. The fact that they were considered for the Swedish national side in 1965 cut no ice with discerning Athletico fans. During that period of Swedish football, you could get in the national squad by postal application.

Left to right: Swedish starlets Benny, Agnetha, Bjorn (top) and Hans

The brothers also refused to give up seal culling between October and April and were seen at 'The Tip' even less than the manager. Naturally, with a weakened squad for so much of the season, Athletico's promotion challenge had to wait but, sinking deeper into debt, it came as no surprise when Homstat's contract was flushed down the loo and the Larssons were told they were no longer fjordable.

So 1968/69 loomed and Reg Pybus seemed the natural choice to take over as manager. But a boardroom vote of six to one in favour was not enough to secure him the position. Ken Mentle, who often made up club rules as he went along, declared that his was the casting vote and promptly blocked the appointment, incredibly naming himself as manager.

Fans were stunned and Pybus' resignation was expected before the start of the new season. However, after a lively meeting with directors, Reg was persuaded to carry on as coach by three men in a hearse who asked to meet him outside during a beer break.

By the opening game, a rare 2–2 draw with Racing Club Barnesfield, Mentle had sacked himself. Continually fighting in and out the dug-out, bickering over team selection and a 1954 Ford Popular, the Mentle/Pybus partnership was completely unworkable. With Ken's second-hand car business booming – 'turn the clock back with Mentle Motors' – he was happy to relieve command.

Dynamic accountant Julian Ripley-Rust came in as team manager and commercial adviser to the club. Rust had good financial credentials and the requisite limited knowledge of football. Desperate for cash following the Swedish debacle, he was one of the first to take on commercial sponsorship by negotiating a less than lucrative deal with Lovetts Panty Hose Ltd, and solely responsible for the bankrupting record fiasco when, at crippling expense, the team took on the guise of the Whaddon Promotion All Stars, and released a record, *Go Go Athletic-O*.

On Saturdays we turn out in our yellow and black strip,
To the chantin' of the faithful few down at 'The Tip'.
There's always lots of action tho' football is a plus,
We've never been to Wembley but we've seen it from a
  bus.

Go Go Go Athletico,
Go Go Go Go for goal.
They say we are the turkeys but you better believe,
We'll be doing all the stuffing,
In the Mid-Counties Combination League.

The record, many copies of which still turn up among the ditches and hedgerows at the leafier end of Whaddon, portrayed a hope and optimism belied by bailiffs at the turnstiles, and its hummability led players and supporters to see the coming season and decade as the dawning of a new age.

LES IN CONFIDENCE

MONDAY, 5th OCTOBER

Trying to compose myself, before concocting the programme notes for the Gosling Celtic match, I notice that I have developed a bad case of the shakes. This may, of course, be due to alcoholic withdrawal but then again perhaps it is a nervous reaction to the hell of this past week.

Those scumbags at the Public Health office sprang an inspector on us last Wednesday. Despite the fact that the showers were writhing with the flabby excesses of Whaddon British Legion 'B' and Mitchley Fire Brigade Dynamoes, this idiot insisted on carrying out his inspection. I thought it a touch of inspiration on my part insisting that he remove all his clothing, 'in the interests of hygiene'. Naturally I never thought the daft sod would, and so there was nothing for it, I had to do likewise and follow him, à la buff, into the showers. The whole thing was a total bloody fiasco. As if the stench of stale sweat and stagnant liniment was not enough, I had to endure the grotesque sensation of his sodden sodding notepad disintegrating between my toes. Luckily, despite the cramped conditions, I was able to block the inspector's view, thereby obscuring Colin Webley's neanderthal plumbing and the various cultures and mould growths my boy Chester has been propagating on the water tank as part of his Tech. college project on legionnaires disease.

Unluckily, neither the inspector nor myself spotted the stray soap and after slipping arse over tit he put his head through the water tank. At this point the rusty trough decided to spew out gallons of ice cold water, panic ensued and 24 naked men made a rush for the exit, much to the astonishment of those still lingering on the touchline after the Wednesday League match.

Was it any wonder I resorted to the drinks cabinet in the director's Portakabin? I only had a couple. A couple of whiskies, a couple of vodkas and a couple of swigs of embrocation. Now, I can hold my liquor as well as the next man, so it is ludicrous to suggest that when I reversed the club van into the tea hut I was under the influence. It was a delusion I was under. What with the shower incident and the strain of management I neglected to recall the fact I could not drive. A simple enough mistake. Anyway, to be on the safe side I have not touched a drop since, but God knows the temptation has been great. Pahdra Singh called me to the club this morning where he and Reg Pybus and their crony, that stingy git Pugh, the corpse planter, unveiled the new team strip. Gawd help us, no wonder the launch was 'shrouded' in mystery: the last time I saw those shirts they were wrapped around the kneelers in Mitchley Crematorium!

REMEMBER: TAKE CHESTER TO THE VET.

ATHLETICO -WHADDON

M/SV. DIVISION 3.

TODAY
· V ·
REDLAND
PARK
AVENUE

£1

* OFFICIAL PROGRAMME *

	P	W	D	L	PTS
ALBORNE	10	6	1	3	19
NORTHTOWN	10	5	3	2	18
GOSLING CELTIC	10	5	3	2	18
REDLAND PARK AVENUE	10	4	4	2	16
CLANSFORD UTD	10	4	4	2	16
FRAMPTON ROVERS	10	4	3	3	15
HELLINGBOROUGH	10	4	2	4	14
FELTON	10	4	1	5	13
DORNING TOWN	10	3	4	3	13
ATH. WHADDON	10	4	1	5	13
SCRIMLEY ARSENAL	10	3	3	4	12
SPORTING HYDRA CHEMICALS	10	2	5	3	11
TWITCHIT ALBION	10	2	4	4	10
LEECH TOWN	10	2	4	4	10
BOTHAM WDRS	10	3	1	6	10
CHAMDEN CITY RESERVES	10	2	3	5	9
SIDCOMBE	10	2	3	5	9

MANAGER'S NOTES

7th November '92

A month is a very long tim in fotbal. It was over for weeks ago that we last publishd a programe, as finansises have been moch two tite for such extragavance.

During this tim the teem hav kept up sum kind of consisstincy by continuwing to loose more games than it haz one. the won-O rouncing by Gozling Celtick was particlely dissappointting tho perhaps no unxpeckeded. Owr unlucky 4-too defeet at Northtown was overshaded by the second sendingoff this season 4 Trever Probe after an hi kicking insident, in which the refereez jaw was broken.

This was only owr fift defeet in ten leeg games (we allso went don 2– at Clansford) so it stood us in good sted for owr Fst rownd match against Drizley Welfare in the 'FARMBOY SHEEP SCAB LINEMENT INTER-LEAGUE TROPHY'. Money of yew will agree that this was owr best proformance of the season so there an owne goal by Davedoyle rite from the kockiff was not a good start but too superherb hedders from Royston Marlee, playing with hevily bandiged neez, one the day four us.

Thowz of u hoo followed us to Hemlock Valley Crusaders for round two must like me. Have espeariensed a sense of day-o shavu as daveDoyle poot the Crusaders ahed with another of hiz cracking owne goles. This tim however we was unabel to mustard owr yewshul gravel and detriment and so went out thre30–.

*   *   *   *   *

Spiking of losses Colin Webley, the club kipper has now returned to his favorit posishun behind the T-counter. Colin

Who, only took up fotbal this seeson has licked nothin in yuthanasium (110$ purr mach) but sadlee could not adap to this hi standard of footee.

* *   *   *   *** *   *

May I tak this opoortuneity to silence those dictators of owr acting person Mr. PD Sing. No yes Mr Singe is dedicated to the fewcher of Athletes Whaddon and to proove it has prezented me with a BLANK czech for £53–24p only, which is at my dispozal for strainthning the squid.
WELL DON MR SINHG

*   *   *   1*

Thow owr leeg campain is priority I have a snee king feeling that this year could be owr year for cup gory. Wee begin owr long March to Wimble wembley next tuesday when we take on hifiying Clutton Town in the preliminary liminary first Qualifying Round of the Fa cup. Kikkup 3 70 a.m.

*   *   ********

Finale may I xtend a heart felt wellcome back to owr chairman Mr. Kin Mental. Tho still farr from competent a 110£ recovery Ken returns today to his beloved Tipp and know dobt the familyer sound of his ukelelelele will be unentertaining us wonse more at halftime. WELL COME BACK SODN.

Thanx mussed also go to the Mitchley Road Primary Skool printing clubb four taking over the produckshun of owr programe. I hope the yungstirs do not hav much dribble with the difficult wurds.

LEZ BONCE

SPOTLIGHT ON ATHLETICO
WHADDON 1970–1979

Athletico Whaddon (1970) Ltd rose from the cheque books of Ken Mentle and Julian Ripley-Rust. The team that ended the 1960s was dumped, and Ripley-Rust and Pybus set about the daunting task of building a squad capable of winning promotion when the club's League career got underway again.

As a result of their financial difficulties, Athletico were forced to resign from the Mid-Counties League and for the 70/71 season played no football at all, thereby suffering no defeats and thus securing their most successful season ever.

Matchless, they spent the season to good effect, scouring the reserve benches of Swansons Sweet Pickle Albion and their ilk. By July they had managed to sign a nucleus of nine players and re-applied to join the Mid-Counties League. However, by some strange quirk of FA paperwork they found themselves in the Multivite Vegeburger/Singletons Valve Replacement League, formerly the Mid-Counties South-West (Northern Division) whose Premier Division Athletico had briefly graced in 1938.

So, as the 71/72 season dawned, Athletico found themselves with a new team, a new league and a bright future. Their opening fixture was a home match against Potley Town and the club decided that this was the day to wake up Whaddon to its new go-ahead football team.

At 2.30p.m. in the Fine Fare car park, a procession mustered. The Whaddon and Mitchley Scouts and Guides band wound its tuneless way along the High Street, followed by six young girls lethally wielding pom-poms – the Mentle Motors Majorettes – and bringing up the rear, Reg Pybus' Bedford minibus in which, crammed like sardines, the new team sat invisible behind the heavily steamed up windows.

Owing to faulty traffic lights at the top of Tip Lane, the procession was held up and, on arriving at the ground, found Potley already on the pitch and themselves a hefty fine for their late arrival for the game. To cap this day of celebration, the 'Whads' went down 4–0 and manager Julian Ripley-Rust was sacked.

Reg took over as caretaker-manager but after only ten minutes of their second match realised that Athletico were out of their depth in Division One and, sure enough, the club was bundled into the Second, finishing the season fifteen points adrift at the bottom.

Pybus was duly sacked but retained as club coach in a refreshment-making capacity. As season 72/73 arrived, a passing shopper, Mrs Hilda Sheppey (58), suddenly found herself the first manageress in football history. Hilda, known affectionately as the 'blue rinse boss', was, to everyone's surprise, to enjoy three seasons in charge at 'The Tip'. Under her direction, the squad became a very close-knit affair comprising as it did four cousins, six nephews and a younger brother (42). The core of the team remained virtually unchanged throughout her reign: Sheppey, Holt, Sheppey, Rawlings, Sheppey, Rawlings, Rawlings, Sheppey, Sheppey, Rawlings, Von Bopp.

Despite a certain amount of success, including a best-ever tenth in the league (73/74), when the board decided to switch training from Tuesday to Thursday Hilda was forced to resign, as it would clash with her night out at bingo.

Once more Reg Pybus was given command and many believed he had inherited one of the great Whaddon sides. Unfortunately, the discovery that young, vivacious, Tania Sheppey was about to enter motherhood, courtesy of centre-half Brian Rawlings, brought about a family rivalry that spilled over on to the football pitch, notably during a League game against Thornham Bridge.

Sheppey A., Sheppey K., Rawlings P., Rawlings B., and Von Bopp were sent off for fighting amongst themselves along with Thornham Bridge captain (later with Athletico), Trevor Proby, who hit everybody. Surprisingly the remaining 'Whads', Holt T., Sheppey S., Rawlings G., Sheppey R., Sheppey V., and Rawlings D., held out to secure an astonishing 2–0 draw in the Bridge's favour.

After such an intolerable display, all those involved in the incident were sacked and Reg Pybus was left to rebuild as best he could.

Over the next few seasons debts continued to mount and in an unprecedented move Athletico again made history, becoming the first club to introduce the £1 pork pie. The players also felt the pinch. A proposed cut in wages was doubled, they were charged 25 pence for the half-time orange and were required to leave a £35 deposit when they took their kit home for washing.

Somehow, despite his regular sacking, Reg managed to keep the club in Division Two. In 77/78 he relinquished the hot seat to former Grundle Ferry Dynamo boss, Roy Alderman, and then the following season to Rabbi Lionel Cohen, who never attended a Saturday match on religious grounds. But by the end of the decade he was once more in charge.

Unable to pay his playing staff, crisis followed crisis but as the 1980s arrived, dramatic changes were about to unfold. These changes were seen by players and supporters alike as the dawning of a new age.

SPOTLIGHT ON THE
SUPPORTERS' CLUB

As anyone involved in football knows, the backbone of a good team is a good manager (Matt Busby, Kenny Dalglish, Les Bence). The dynamic diaphragm of any club, however, is its support, those diehards who, for no reward, man the gates, pick up litter, kick back the divots and aerosol the toilets. These are the dedicated few who, week in, week out, come rain or snow, stare out of the clubhouse window at 22 diehards freezing their pads off for fun.

Athletico formed its own official Supporters' Club in 1953. It was founded by Stan Barnet and Sid Dicker and in the early days met behind the grandstand on match days. They gained a permanent home in 1961 when the groundsman's hut became vacant. Unfortunately, it could only accommodate six people and a crate of Nettles Agricultural Sherry so, as membership grew, tempers were often explosive and much precious nectar was spilt.

The turning point came in 1972 when Ken Mentle dug deep into his pocket and bought a deluxe Portakabin for directors and players, and the Supporters' Club was given the drain end as its new home. This move brought players and fans into regular contact, and the board presented one young supporter, Leslie Bence, with life membership after he was spotted by the team at an away match.

It was not long before the club became a social 'Mecca' for the local community. Bingo, skittles, old-tyme Kung-fu, spitting at the chicken, all ensured that the club's calendar was full for 370 days a year. There have been many great events to remember over the years. The 1976 Open Blow-Football Tournament, won by a crack Whaddon WI team, springs to mind, as does the 1974 Christmas jumble sale which received a four-star review in the Oxfam magazine.

Then who can forget those cabaret evenings? Remember topless rock and roll with Victor Shrigley and his Giggly Wigglies. Bottomless sing-a-longs with Bob Sedgemoor and his organ, or those popular Country and Western evenings with Whaddon's own 'Belle of the Canteena', Rosetta Fish, or the singing house conveyors, Deceptively Spacious Tex Mortgage and the Black Gulch Estate Agents.

Yes, when it comes to social events, the Athletico Supporters' Club can feel rightly proud.

Rev. V. Shrigley
Soc. Sec.

LES IN CONFIDENCE

THURSDAY, 5th NOVEMBER

I have just taken a long, stiff drink. About a litre long and as stiff as Liberace. I warned the board that privatising the programme production would be a disaster. Scully and Sons have had the job for as long as I can remember, not because they are any good but because they are ruddy cheap. Old man Scully has not put his prices up since 1947 and he probably bought his printing set from John Bull himself. It was Pybus who had the brilliant idea of putting the thing out to tender and, despite my warnings, thought that no one could match the school's price of 158 banana chews, free strawberry milkshakes once a week during the season and a promise from Mike Channon that he would play the Virgin Mary in the school nativity play. Well, Reg and Singh were very quiet when I showed them what those little brats had produced. Hells bells! they could not even spell teem! We managed to salvage the Spotlight feature but my bloody notes had already been printed. They had nothing for it but to crawl back to Mr Scully and to pay Mike Channon's cancellation fee (£353) out of their own pockets.

If this club wants to know how to make money then it ought to listen to my boy Chester. At his suggestion we will be holding a car boot sale at 'The Tip' in the near future. He tells me that it is a dead cert, we can make an absolute killing by taking a percentage of the profits, and charging pitch holders a rip-off rent. Details have still to be worked out, but Chez reckons that with the aid of his home computer and his Nintendo Boot Sale Blitz game, he and I can milk off a tidy sum whilst still leaving the club with a small profit. It is good to see Chester growing up in my image. I have noticed how close we have grown since his mother ran off with the Turnbury Post Office United's physiotherapist.

This boot sale is such a good idea I think I might have my own pitch and run a Help The Aged stall. I am sure I could sting this town's senile pensioners for a couple of quid, by selling them the old tea hut as firewood. It would certainly get it out of the back of my Reliant. After the fiasco over the programmes I shall take full control of this project and set up my headquarters in the Jessie Matthews Lounge at the Duck and Forceps.

Colin Webley called round earlier at my request. I decided to be tactful and told him he would no longer be considered for the team because he is complete and utter rubbish. I told him there were no hard feelings and that I was only thinking of the club, blah, blah, blah. To soften the blow I said it was only because I was held in such high esteem in the football world that I had to get rid of any player or, as in his case, friend, who showed any sign of being a no-hoper. It was my duty to nurture and encourage only those with potential and he had about as much as a Mike Channon betting tip.

Webley was visibly shocked but I assured him he could still continue to wash the team strip every week.

I am just an old softie at heart.

ATHLETICO -WHADDON

M/SV. DIVISION 3.

TODAY
· V ·
SIDCOMBE

£1

* OFFICIAL PROGRAMME *

	P	W	D	L	PTS
CLANSFORD UTD	16	9	4	3	31
GOSLING CELTIC	16	8	5	3	29
ALBORNE	16	7	5	4	26
SCRIMLEY ARSENAL	16	7	4	5	25
NORTHTOWN	16	7	4	5	25
HELLINGBOROUGH	16	7	3	6	24
REDLAND PARK AVENUE	16	6	6	4	24
FRAMPTON ROVERS	16	6	4	6	22
LEECH TOWN	16	5	6	5	21
SPORTING HYDRA CHEMICALS	16	5	5	6	20
TWITCHIT ALBION	16	5	4	7	19
BOTHAM WDRS	16	6	1	9	19
FELTON	15	5	3	7	18
DORNING TOWN	15	4	6	5	18
CHAMDEN CITY RESERVES	16	3	5	8	14
ATH. WHADDON	14	4	1	9	13
SIDCOMBE	16	2	6	8	12

MANAGER'S NOTES

16th January '93

Welcome back to 'The Tip', everybody.

The reasons for our absence over the last month or more have been well documented in the local gutter press, and through the many acrimonious exchanges between club and supporters. Back at the beginning of November we instigated our first car boot sale, which we reluctantly accept was less than a 110 per cent success. Heavy rain the night before meant the pitch was waterlogged, and a misunderstanding between the groundsman and myself led to his directing all vehicles on to the playing area. Many of these cars had to be towed off by a tractor which, like our forward line, itself became bogged down in midfield. With the pitch resembling a motocross track, we had no option but to postpone our home games with Dorning Town and Felton. This resulted in a hefty fine being imposed by the county FA, on top of a fine for fielding an ineligible player during the match at Twitchit Albion.

Once again our chairman, Mr Ken Mentle, has been called upon to bale us out but, unlike the current state of our penalty area, his wallet is not a bottomless pit.

*　　　*　　　*　　　*　　　*　　　*　　　*

When you witness the amount of effort and skill our lads ignite every match with, it is astonishing that our League results in our absence from 'The Tip' have been a string of defeats. Losing 1–0, 5–3 and 2–0 to Redland Park Avenue, Botham Wanderers, and Twitchit Albion respectively means that promotion may now be beyond our grasp.

Yet these results seem quite astonishing if you cast your mind back to our last appearance at 'The Tip'. It was then that we took on the giants of the Premier Division, Clutton Town, in the FA Cup. They left 'The Tip' if you recall, with egg on their faces after securing a pitiful 6–2 victory over us. Many Clutton players and supporters were still stunned by Royston Marley's brilliant brace of goals as they boarded the bus home. I am sure you are all aware that Royston is an important cog in the Athletico jigsaw and his recurrent knee injury has played a large part in our poor results this season. On behalf of the club, I have approached Ross Chicken Ltd in the hope that 'Royst' may be relieved from his job as a chicken sexer and a more 'knee-friendly' task found for him.

*   *   *   *   *   *   *

Such is the lot of the football manager that constant criticism has to be lived with. Recently, my managerial integrity has been called into question by a number of directors and supporters. Their concern relates to my dismissing the former club captain, Colin Webley. After many years dispensing tea to supporters, Colin took up football with the club this season and, to boost his confidence, I appointed him skipper. After six competitive games it became clear to me that the standard of football required in the Multivite/Singletons League Division Three was way beyond his ability and so, sadly, I felt the club was no longer able to accommodate him as a player. I am as surprised as anyone to learn that Colin has now signed for current Football League champions Leeds United.

Since this news broke, I have been subjected to numerous snide remarks concerning my ability to spot a footballer when I see one. Let me make it clear, football is a game played by one team against another with a ball. It requires planning, skill and tactics to create a winning side and if the individual players do not fit into the maze, if they cannot work within a cohesive unit, then success will elude the whole team. With limited resources I am striving to build a ruthless goal-scoring machine. There is no place for a quality footballer if he believes he is more than just a page in that machine. No individual, apart from myself, is bigger than this club.

*   *   *   *   *   *   *

Although results are running against us, surely today, against bottom club Sidcombe, who narrowly defeated us 3–0 earlier this season, we can record our fifth win of the present campaign.

SPOTLIGHT ON ATHLETICO
WHADDON 1980–1992

1980 brought yet another new manager in Ken Smith, local farmer and playboy. Smith's first task was to improve the ground's facilities. Plans were put into action to buy and erect floodlights, but more importantly to install toilets, as the constant 'watering' of the oak tree behind the grandstand was causing it to rot away and sway, menacingly, over the directors' seats. Regrettably, Ken Mentle handed over the money to Smith and, as well as manager, appointed him club development officer. By the time it was discovered that Smith had used the money to develop the bank accounts of local bookies and the jewellery collections of local ladies of ill repute, it was too late. The club managed to recoup £304, and this was spent on a single floodlight. Smith's dismissal put Reg Pybus back in charge for the rest of the season, the undoubted highlight of which was a special match held to celebrate the turning on of the floodlight. Athletico took on the toughest of opposition by playing a Darlington Groundstaff XI. The Mayor, Ivor Cuth, placed the last of 150 U2 batteries in position, and the light was switched on. A magnificent crowd of 83 witnessed the ceremony, 32 of them staying for the match. The event started with a slight hiccup when it was discovered that the batteries were in the wrong way round. Play around the centre spot was fast and furious, though the ground was in total darkness everywhere else. The game was abandoned after fifteen minutes when the ball disappeared in a black hole at the sewage works end.

After another year languishing, knee high, in Division Two, Reg was once again ousted and, for season 82/83, fanatical big mouth and stalwart supporter, Vic Noodle, took over.

Originally, he was on a six-month contract but despite disappointing results he was able to re-negotiate his contract. He married Yvonne Mentle, Ken's daughter. Vic Noodle kicked off married life and the new season by pawning his wife's jewellery and bringing in a clutch of new signings. Although slow and the wrong side of 43, 'Gabby' Hinton was classy and a strong believer in football and family entertainment. To this end, he often smoked his pipe during the game and always insisted on playing in his slippers. Another colourful signing was the Reverend Hubert Jolly, who followed in the footsteps of that other great sporting cleric, W. G. Grace, although W. G. was a cricketer not a footballer and a doctor not a vicar. Jolly was already a well known celebrity, not only for his pre-match evangelising but also for his best-selling books on clerical life, *Vicars in a Twist* and *Bare Butts in the Belfry*. On the field he was extremely competent, having spent years in the forward linc of St Dodimeads Choirboys XI and the Billy Graham Crusade. Later he became a director of the club and built the small chapel behind the groundsman's hut where visiting supporters could find 'quiet contemplation and a cup of Bovril (58p)'.

The most notable of Vic's signings, however, was former Thornham Bridge captain, Trevor Proby. Desperate for players, Athletico were willing to take a chance with Proby and his fiery temper. This was Noodle's big mistake. In thirty outings during the season, Proby's vicious streak, and obsessive belief that all referees were illegitimate, led to him receiving his marching orders no less than eighteen times!

Aware of Trevor's previous record, the FA sentenced him to a 152-match suspension, a ban of four years. Whereas in management I take the raw clay of inexperience, then shape and mould it into a team of teapots, Vic had an old-fashioned approach, plucking players with natural ability and building them into a cohesive unit but where no player's unique, individual flair was stifled. His third and final term opened with

Hard man Trevor Proby reacts philosophically to his four-match ban

great success. Although Whaddon were the only team to enter, and despite the FA declaring the competition null and void, we can, in all fairness I think, claim to have been holders of the Charwoods' Sweet Pickle A and B Cup. That season also saw our best ever run in the FA Cup, reaching the second preliminary, preliminary qualifying round before bowing out 4–0 to Ajax Pan-Shine Combination League champions, Amblewick Carthegians. Good League results led even the club's sternest critic to believe that in Vic Noodle we had found the man to take us into the Football League. Then disaster struck. The *Whaddon and Mitchley Argus*, under the by-line of trainee reporter-cyclist Mark Crowe, revealed that Yvonne Noodle (*née* Mentle), had been carrying on an affair with disgraced Athletico player, Trevor Proby. The paper published photographs, taken by Crowe, from a distance of half a mile, that purported to be of a topless Trevor and a scantily overcoated Yvonne sucking toes on the lawn of

Proby's Thornham Bridge hacienda. Ken Mentle was placed in an awkward situation but saw his loyalties as lying with his daughter. Unbelievably, he sacked his son-in-law and replaced him in the manager's seat with Trevor Proby. This news rocked the Whaddon footballing fraternity and questions were even asked in the house, albeit the Duck and Forceps public house.

Fate, however, now played a striker's role. Trevor was unable to take up his post because, through circumstances beyond the law, he was forced to lie low in the Bahamas for a couple of years. But the damage had been done. Despite free lunches, unlimited use of Ken's chauffeur-driven Lada and the promise of regular wages, Vic Noodle declined the chance to return. Instead he took up a lucrative coaching post with the Botswana Youth team. There was no Reg Pybus to stand in this time, he too had left for pastures new. Manager of Third Division Bowden Mesopotamians.

Pensioner Walter Niblet pulled the dreaded raffle ticket from the bucket to become manager for season 87/88. I personally led a vigorous campaign to get Niblet removed at the first opportunity. I lambasted the board through the letters page of the 'Sporting Mauve' for appointing an octogenarian ignoramus. Sadly, the momentum gathered in the early days of my crusade had fizzled out by April, when it became obvious we were heading for Division One. As it was, my criticism was entirely vindicated. A disastrous run of one defeat in nine games meant we ended the season a pathetic third. Against my advice, Walter, despite being 78, was immediately named manager for 88/89 and this time we were runners-up and promoted.

It was a proud day for 'The Tip' when the dawning of the 89/90 season saw us amongst the Multivite/Singletons élite. That first season back in Division One is still fondly recalled by supporters. Some of the players have already passed into Whaddon's sporting folklore. Names like Dalglish, Gascgoine and Shilton, three jewels in Athletico's crown, are always mentioned in reverential tones on the terraces or in the Anna Neagle Grill and Burger Bar at the Duck and Forceps. Melvin Dalglish, our tussle-haired goalkeeper who had Velcro stuck to the palms of his gloves. Stanley Gascgoine, a green marvel with a two-pronged attack, left foot, right foot or head. Ivor Shilton, a midfield dynamo whose nose glowed in the dark.

Finding the workload too much, 'Nibby' coaxed Reg Pybus back as his assistant, but when Walter Niblet dropped dead during a 3–1 defeat by Red Star Onglethorpe, Ken refused to appoint Reg as caretaker manager. Instead, he put the job back in the raffle. This was to be a momentous decision although he did not know it at the time. With the club now languishing at the bottom of the table they were in desperate need of a football visionary, a new footballing messiah. They needed a miracle and that miracle was me, Les Bence. A life-long supporter, I have always been regarded as a tactical genius by the Duck and Forceps regulars and, from day one, my appointment has brought renewed hope to the terraces.

During my term as manager I have made few friends and my enemies stalk the boardroom in ever increasing numbers. I have survived only on the fantastic loyalty of players and fans. Their loyalty has stayed with me because, despite the disappointment of relegation in 90/91 and our meteoric plummet through Division Two last season, they know that I can in no way be held responsible.

In actual fact, throughout the entire history of Athletico Whaddon, much of the blame for our failure can be placed at the feet of one man, Ken Mentle. Far be it from me to speak ill of the dead but Ken Mentle, may he rest in peace, single-handedly made this club what it is today, the Accrington Stanley of Bradford Park Avenue.

Thank heavens we at last have at the helm a manager of exceptional gifts and a fabulous chairman, Mr Pahdra Singh, who has no interest in soccer. Football needs more men like

Pahdra at the masthead. It needs men who are willing, without question, to say, 'I'll leave it up to you, Les, whatever you say.'

All Pahdra and I require is unquestioning encouragement and support. If we get this, then I see the 1990s as the dawning of a new age for Athletico Whaddon.

LES IN CONFIDENCE

WEDNESDAY, 13th JANUARY 1993

As I sat down to write up my diary a brick arrived through my sitting room window. The window was closed. It is now open. The brick was wrapped in two notes, the first apologised for the mess and the second, bearing Trevor Proby's signature, offered to lend me the £250 the club are still trying to stitch me for after that car boot sale fiasco. I am going to have to take Proby up on his offer but Gawd knows what the interest will be.

Athletico are nothing but money-grabbing bastards. All right, so I took full responsibility for the organisation of the sale, but there is no way I can be blamed for the outcome. As I told the board before their meeting with the Receiver, the blame lies solely with the person who dreamt up the idea, namely Chester Bence. They were not impressed. Still, it taught me a thing or two. For one thing, it is about time that little sod Chester started paying rent to live here — £250 seems to be the going rate these days. He treats this like a dressing room, him and his groundhopping mates. Hardly a day goes by without being neck-high in severely anoraked shop assistants, munching Kit-Kats and watching endless slides of football ground urinals from the length and breadth of Britain. If it's not them, then the house is buried in thousands of paper slips on which he works out leagues and fixtures for his absurd postal blow-football competition.

Things are becoming intolerable at the club these days and the boot sale is only part of it. Our abysmal form has brought calls for my resignation, notably from fatty Singh and his toady Pybus, but also from many supporters. I do not think Ken Mentle's support will survive his clogged arteries. I shall make it clear to those moronic malcontents on the terraces that I have no intention of quitting. I shall bluff it out at least until my next dole cheque. These people seem to forget that results do not mean a thing in football and are only of secondary interest to a manager. In my book the only time a manager should consider resigning is when he starts believing his own programme notes. What these boardroom blouses and toerags at the turnstiles do not realise is that football management is not a skill to be acquired through hard work, but a gift from God. Those blessed with a prophetic vision of soccer's future, like Mike Channon and myself, are often completely ignored or misunderstood, whereas charlatans who would not know one end of a football from another, the Reg Pybuses and Howard Wilkinsons of this world, suck up to mediocrity and call it talent.

When Piedish told me he had secured Webley's transfer to Leeds United, I laughed him out of the Duck and Forceps. It is a joke and I told Wilkinson so. In fact, so contemptible did I find his dismissal of my judgement as to what constitutes talent on the football field, that I flatly refused the £200,000 fee they were willing to pay for Colin Webley and let the useless git go on a free transfer!

REMEMBER: NAME TREV PROBY AS NEW CAPTAIN.

ATHLETICO WHADDON

M/SV. DIVISION 3

TODAY

• V •

CHAMDEN CITY RESERVES

£1

* OFFICIAL PROGRAMME *

	P	W	D	L	PTS
CLANSFORD UTD	18	11	4	3	37
GOSLING CELTIC	18	9	5	4	32
NORTHTOWN	18	8	5	5	29
SCRIMLEY ARSENAL	18	8	4	6	28
HELLINGBOROUGH	18	8	3	7	27
ALBORNE	18	7	6	5	27
REDLAND PARK AVENUE	18	6	7	5	25
TWITCHIT ALBION	18	7	4	7	25
SPORTING HYDRA CHEMICALS	18	6	6	6	24
LEECH TOWN	18	6	6	6	24
FRAMPTON ROVERS	18	6	5	7	23
FELTON	17	6	3	8	21
DORNING TOWN	17	5	6	6	21
CHAMDEN CITY RESERVES	18	5	5	8	20
BOTHAM WDRS	18	6	2	10	20
SIDCOMBE	18	3	6	9	15
ATH. WHADDON	16	4	1	11	13

MANAGER'S NOTES

30th January '93

Ken Mentle, a 'Stiff' to the end

It is with deep regret that, on behalf of Athletico Whaddon Football Club, I have to report the death of club chairman, Mr Ken Mentle. Forty-two years as a devoted servant to this club is an astonishing record and Ken's dedication to and belief in Athletico is an example to everyone in the world of football. The loss to the game, through his sad departure to that great boardroom in the sky, is incalculable. Ken's enthusiasm never diminished and up until his recent heart trouble his work rate for the club was never less than 114 per cent. Ironically, he was on the way to a full recovery when he choked on a curry bone at acting chairman, Mr Pahdra Singh's, restaurant. Although still in a state of shock, Mr

Singh has now appointed himself to the full chairmanship and, along with myself, represented the club at the funeral. Mr Singh's appointment was unanimously approved by the board following the resignation of long-time directors, taxi owner Fred Tilley and poodle manicurist Raymonde Carter. Their positions have now been filled by Mr Namadra Singh and Mr Giljod Singh, neither of whom, surprisingly, are related to the chairman.

*　　　*　　　*　　　*　　　*　　　*　　　*

Chairman Singh's cash injection of £53.24, back in November, has brought no less than FOUR new players to the club. Clive Smott (59) was formerly with Princess Eugene Road Garage Reserves and has agreed to come out of retirement and put on his boots for the first time in three years. Wayne Pollock (38) is a young, exciting defender who nevertheless believes, like me, in some of football's older values like neat hair and shorts down past his knees. Darren Pugh is the nephew of Mr Pugh, partner in Lonsdale and Pugh, undertakers and, of course, our sponsors. This should assure him of a bright future with 'The Stiffs' and, in all probability, lead to the club captaincy next season. Darren, who is only thirteen and ineligible to play, looks seventeen and so should fool League officials. Finally, new boy number four, and our most exciting capture in years, Miguel Romerez (34). Miguel joins us direct from BARCELONA, where he lived for several months. The talented Spaniard has just opened a pizza parlour in the town and has not played football before. However, it is a well known fact that all Spanish men are born with a football in their mouth and so I am sure his dormant skills will blossom forth as soon as he walks out on to the park.

*　　　*　　　*　　　*　　　*　　　*　　　*

What an outstanding performance our home game with Sidcombe turned out to be a fortnight ago. We outclassed them in every department except one, goal-scoring, as their three to our none all too clearly showed. Many, like myself, thought we were unlucky to be the victims of Sidcombe's third victory of the season. At least it stood us in good stead for Tuesday night's game at Scrimley Arsenal, where we came away with a very creditable 2–4 defeat. Once again Royston Marley proved his class by netting both our goals with deflections off his deadly bottom. The amount of running he put in was quite remarkable when you remember that, on his doctor's advice, his knees were strapped together.

*   *   *   *   *   *   *

The foot of the League is beginning to take on a familiar appearance as far as Athletico is concerned:

	P	W	D	L	PTS
Chamden Res	18	5	5	8	20
Botham Wdrs	18	6	2	10	20
Sidcombe	18	3	6	9	15
Ath. Whaddon	16	4	1	11	13

However, I feel there is another way to look at it:

	P	W	D	L	PTS
Ath. Whaddon	16	4	1	11	13
Sidcombe	18	3	6	9	15
Botham Wdrs	18	6	2	10	20
Chamden Res	18	5	5	8	20

*   *   *   *   *   *   *

Today we entertain fellow strugglers, Chamden City Reserves, who we beat on the opening day of the season. They cannot match our record of ten defeats in a row, having staged something of a revival with three straight victories.

Following our disastrous Boxing Day at Leech Town (0–1) and equally poor start to the New Year, we are hoping for a turn in fortune today or, even at this late stage, postponement through frost.

YOUR LINE TO LES

Dear Leslie,

I am just a humble supporter who, though never blessed with the gift myself, loves the artistry and beauty of football and the poetry in motion displayed by the Athletico forward line.

I have often succumbed to the graceful, bronzed beauty of Michael Deere and Terence Wade's limbs as they power into action and imagine not John Motson or Alan Hansen commentating on another blistering attack, but David Attenborough in mildly hushed tones, comparing our boys with leaping gazelles or sprightly cheetahs. Do they affect you in the same way?

Yours, K.D.

Dear K.D.,

Gazelles? Cheetahs? How rare to find an aesthete and intellectual artisan, much like myself, on the terraces these days.

Too many people believe football is nothing more than a game, but you and I know it to be so much more. Somebody once said (Mick Channon?) that in the footballer's craft he saw 'The personification of nature in all its multivariant elements. The juxtaposition of art and realism, of beauty and brutality.' How true that is.

Throughout history football has been the favoured sport of the artistic community. As is well known, the Italians are soccer mad and so it is a fair bet that come Saturday, Michaelangelo would forsake the Cistern Chapel and Leonardo Di Vinci break off from designing the clockwork egg slicer and instead be found occupying the terraces of Inter-Milan or Juventus.

Yours, Leslie 'Bragg' Bence

Dear Les,

Let me come straight to the point. I am not a person to beat about the bush. I like to say what I have to say in as few words as possible and to lay my cards on the table for all to see. Terry Wade, get rid of him, Les.

Now I have nothing against Terry as a person, although I do not think I would cross the road to help him if he were run over by a lorry, but that is neither here nor there. It is the football that counts and frankly, me and the other two regulars are not impressed.

Somebody once said, I think it was you, Les, that football is all about attitude. We do not like Terry's. It is not for the likes of us to try and tell you your job, after all, you are the boss and it is your decision as to who gets in the squad, but when rubbish like Terry becomes a regular, well . . . it reflects on the whole team and your lousy judgement in particular. It will, I know, be a tough decision for you to make, Les, because it is common knowledge that Terry has you in his back pocket, but he is the weak link in the team this year. The round peg in a square forward line. He has to be dropped. Surely you can tap the chairman for a few quid so we can buy someone half-decent.

Yours faithfully,
V. Wade (Mrs)

Dear Mrs Wade,

Just because unsubstantiated rumours abound that Terry's brother Ted occasionally supplies me with specialist literature from the Continent, it does not mean I am taking backhanders or looking favourably towards Terry when including him in the first team.

With respect, I see myself as a master craftsman, but even craftsmen need quality tools to produce a work of art. I see my job here at 'The Tip' as akin to building the Taj Mahal from scratch.

Yours-in-hope,
LES BENCE

Dear Les,
Although you have not been in the manager's seat very long, you have done nothing to alter my original opinion that your appointment makes about as much sense as the Charge of the Light Brigade.

I love this club and so only wish to offer encouragement. However, I enclose a petition signed by 11,000 inhabitants (95 per cent of the local population) demanding your resignation by second post today.

Good luck,
R. Pybus (no relation)

Dear Reg,
So it was your petition I signed the other day, was it?

Since receiving a copy I have scrutinised it with a fine toothpick and believe the whole thing to be completely bogus. Although our home gates of between 26 and 130 are the envy of many a Football League club, they only represent 0.25 per cent of those who put their names to your petition. People will sign anything, son.

In all my days as a Whaddon resident I do not recall a Descartes family in the neighbourhood and surely (please God) there cannot be two Keith Chegwins in the world?

What really sets this up as a fraud and complete load of tripe, is the ridiculous assumption on the part of the forger, that my entire squad of players would happily sign a document whose sole aim is to get me removed from the manager's seat.

THE BOSS

LES IN CONFIDENCE

WEDNESDAY, 27th JANUARY

My loyalty to Athletico amazes even me sometimes. Despite clashing with my dole day, I had no hesitation in forgoing it to attend Ken Mentle's funeral.

Like every other funeral I have attended, laughs were few and the weather was bloody awful. Things got off to a bad start anyway when my Reliant Robin was crushed by Pahdra Singh's Bentley as we jostled for a parking place. Things got very heated as I demanded he pay me full compensation. Singh refused, saying he had no idea there was a car already in the space, all he had seen was a Reliant. In the end we compromised, Singh apologised and I agreed to pay for repairs to his side-light.

Looking back on it, perhaps it was not appropriate for me to heckle the vicar over the inadequate parking facilities at St Dodimeads. A number of mourners were quite abusive after the service and if I had not found the funeral so moving I would of asked one or two to step into the vestry.

Ken's last wish was that his coffin should be carried by six Athletico players but I could not find a single one of the bastards who would do it for less than fifty quid. At least Trevor Proby had a reasonable excuse, he was decorating Pahdra Singh's house. (I wonder why Pahdra wanted an antique and bric-a-brac dealer to hang his wallpaper?) In the end, Lonsdale and Pugh's usual crew did the honours and old Pugh played 'You'll Never Walk Alone' on the organ. Even I shed a tear when the coffin was carried from the church to a recording of Jack Charlton's 'Geordie Sunday'.

Mrs Mentle and I both felt it was touching of Pugh to place a sticker in the back of the hearse which read 'Don't follow me, follow Athletico Whaddon.' She was also touched to think the club were going to display his ukelele in the trophy cabinet. I did not have the heart to tell her that Ken's beloved instrument was now a thousand tiny splinters after Trev Proby sat on it.

The service at the crematorium went off like a house on fire and on returning home I received a phone call from Pybus to say that, at a meeting of directors, Carter and Tilley had quit. It seems extraordinary that as manager I was not invited to attend, yet Reg, a mere team coach and raffle organiser, was.

As it was, I already knew of their resignation as both had phoned me to see if I would give them backing in a boardroom coup. They offered me considerable incentives to take up the role of figurehead in the new Whaddon regime; unlimited and free use of Tilley's taxis between 2.30 and 4.15 on Tuesday afternoons and generous discounts should I ever need the cat coiffured. However, I made my position very clear to the *Whaddon and Mitchley Argus* sports hack, Mark Crowe, when he came sniffing round at the funeral. 'Football to me,' I said, 'is about 22 fit men kicking a ball around a park, not about pot-bellied Freemasons passing the sherry decanter around a centrally heated Portakabin.' Even that buttock-licker Pybus seems worried that Pahdra Singh has replaced them with his shifty brothers but, as I told Crowe, having a property developer, an estate agent and a supermarket magnate on the board can only be good for the club.

My genius never fails to amaze. Four new players and Singh's miserly £53.23 safely deposited in my bank account, although he might ask for it back when he sees the crap I have signed. Old body disposer Pugh's nephew Duncan has been begging me for months to let him play and things have got so desperate I have no choice but to take him on. The fact that he is under-age could be a problem but a false beard, grey wig and strap-on paunch should be enough to fool any referee likely to officiate at an Athletico game. Mig Romerez did not even recognise a football when I showed him one but his exotic appearance should be enough to impress those bumpkins in 'The Tip' crowd. His pizza slices certainly rekindle memories of the good old days in football ... they taste like Dubbin. As for Wayne Pollock and Clive Smott, they are totally unknown quantities. In actual fact, I cannot even remember signing them! I must have bloody done so, because they both produced contracts and five or six witnesses who swore that, although I was completely paralytic, I signed them on last Monday night at the Duck and Forceps.

Pahdra Singh has just called to say that while he was at the funeral his house was burgled and a number of valuable antiques were stolen.

REMEMBER: TAKE CHESTER TO VET.

ATHLETICO
-WHADDON
M/SV.
DIVISION 3
TODAY
•V•
FRAMPTON
ROVERS
£1
* OFFICIAL PROGRAMME *

	P	W	D	L	PTS
CLANSFORD UTD	19	12	4	3	40
GOSLING CELTIC	19	10	5	4	35
NORTHTOWN	19	9	5	5	32
SCRIMLEY ARSENAL	19	8	5	6	29
ALBORNE	19	7	7	5	28
HELLINGBOROUGH	19	8	3	8	27
FRAMPTON ROVERS	19	7	5	7	26
REDLAND PARK AVENUE	19	6	7	6	25
TWITCHIT ALBION	19	7	4	8	25
LEECH TOWN	19	6	7	6	25
SPORTING HYDRA CHEMICALS	19	6	6	7	24
DORNING TOWN	18	6	6	6	24
CHAMDEN CITY RESERVES	19	6	5	8	23
FELTON	18	6	4	8	22
BOTHAM WDRS	19	6	3	10	21
SIDCOMBE	19	3	6	10	15
ATH. WHADDON	17	4	1	12	13

MANAGER'S NOTES

6th February '93

Once again, following our 1–0 defeat against Chamden City Reserves, the more bewildered of our supporters have subjected myself and other club officials to hysterical abuse and spit.

We ALL want the team to do well and, although results are going against us at present, I feel my policy of rebuilding will, in the long term, bring us success. There can be no instant cure. All right, the team are going through a temporary loss of form and that is not what you pay to see but, remember, football is a business not an entertainment. After saying that, I am sure every fan was heartened by the performance of our new quartet. The players, I know, especially enjoyed Miguel's tasty pizza slices at half-time.

*　　　　*　　　　*　　　　*　　　　*　　　　*　　　　*

Our leading goal-scorer, Royston Marley, is sadly on the move back to his native West Indies following receipt of special transfer forms. These forms are known as a Deportation Order. Unbeknownst to club officials, 'Royst' was in fact only a visitor to this country and his permit ran out two months ago. His departure will, of course, be a serious blow to our hopes of pulling away from the foot of the table. The return of 'Mad' Trevor 'Killer' Proby after another lengthy suspension should plug the gaping hole currently occupying our defence. Let us hope Trevor can surprise us all and stay on the park until the end of the season. It is through my perceptive ability to spot talent where others fail, that in signing Clive Smott, son of former manager Wally, I have found the perfect replacement for Royston Marley. Many of you, I know, believe

Smott's substitution after four minutes was because he was out of his depth, but I can assure you it is all part of my master plan which I am painstakingly developing on a game-by-game basis. I am more than a little confident that its fruition will be more than evident before the last kick of the season.

*　　　　*　　　　*　　　　*　　　　*　　　　*　　　　*

May I take this opportunity to dispel rumours, circulating among supporters, concerning Mr Pahdra Singh's involvement with an unnamed supermarket syndicate which is believed to be interested in purchasing 'The Tip' for redevelopment. Mr Singh has strongly denied these allegations in the Press and wishes to do so again. Unfortunately, fair-weather supporters tend to forget that no Athletico official gives less than 110 per cent to the club week in, Sundays off, and to think their heads could be turned in the hope of making financial personal gain is an insult.

CHAIRMAN'S CHAT

A jubilant Pahdra at a recent home game

Firstly, may I thank Mr Bence and the editors for allowing me a few lines in which to formally meet you all.

Although I have been a member of the board for less than a year, and chairman but a few weeks, I believe I have now been accepted into the bosom of the Athletico family. Were I to meet any of you at the golf club or the Mayor's banquet I am sure we could talk as equals over a glass of sherry and a snipe sandwich.

As the delegated head of this wonderful club, I see my duties as follows: firstly to my wife and children; secondly to other members of my family; then to consolidate my assets in any profitable manner I choose; and then to devote the rest of my time to the welfare of this club.

Though some of you may question my priorities we must be under no illusion. As that 'winger of wisdom' Leslie Bence has so often pointed out, football is a business. Luckily for Athletico, business is my business and something at which I excel, as many of you will know from the success of my 8-Day Superette in the High Street. Talking of which, this week Family Shopper Coffee Granules are only 64 pence a jar.

I know you see which side my fence is buttered, and if I can bring to football the organisational skills that have made me such a big fish in retailing, then Athletico Whaddon need have no fear of ending up on the slab.

But what of the criticism so often levelled at Leslie and myself that we have no idea how to run a football club? Well, my answer to this is simple. It was of no importance to the success of my Superette that I did not know how Spratts Processed Peas were manufactured, therefore when running a football team it can be of no importance if Leslie and I do not know how many players it contains.

As I have mentioned them, may I just point out that Spatts Peas are delicious with chipped potatoes or an omelette or simply naked from the tin. They are also four pence cheaper at my Superette than anywhere else in Whaddon.

As a businessman, it would be foolhardy of me to pour my own money nilly-willy into the club and so I am constantly on the look-out for companies willing to risk investing in a lowly but forward-looking team. We are grateful for the loose change of Messrs Lonsdale and Pugh, but let me assure you all, with a family-sized packet of Fisherman's Friend extra throat lozenges placed firmly on my heart, that I will strive in ever-decreasing circles to bring the sponsorship of a major international to 'The Tip' to provide much needed support to our glorious team.

All I ask is that you are patient. Leslie Bence is a man with the gift of impaired vision, a vision that will take time to grow and expand. If you have forgotten this article within the next hour remember, please, just two things. Firstly, that as chairman of Athletico Whaddon I will never devote less than 36 per cent of my time to the club and, secondly, there are, this season, substantial discounts to any supporter spending over £20 at my Superette. Happy football and happy shopping.

PAHDRA

ATHLETICO WHADDON – THE GREAT GAMES

Les Bence looks at some of the great matches he has witnessed.

September 1992
CHAMDEN CITY RESERVES 1, ATHLETICO WHADDON 2

When I suggested this feature for the programme in the club-house, I was amazed no one put forward a match from my period as manager. Therefore to kick off this irregular feature I have chosen one myself – as it happens, the first game of this season.

Was it only five months ago we were all talking of promotion as a certainty? In my position you soon learn that football has only one certainty, that at the end of ninety minutes the final whistle blows unless there is extra time.

As you will recall, I have persistently warned you all about taking promotion for granted and I am sure if you read back over my programme notes you will find I have not once alluded to it. Having said that, the vague possibility that we may end this season by finishing bottom and going out of the League remains incomprehensible to me and I am at a loss to explain it.

How different it all seemed back in September, though. A new season, a new League and a great bit of luck. Chamden City Reserves could only find five players. From July onwards the town of Whaddon had waited with bated breath. Expectation had been rampant throughout June but, come the pre-season friendlies of August, football fever had reached dizzy heights. Those warm-up games had given no indication of the glory to come.

Expectation was boiling when we all climbed into Reg's minibus and headed for Chamden on that balmy September Saturday. Behind us, the fanatical 'Whaddon Army' piled into the social club's Morris Minor and the black-and-yellow horde sped along the Mitchley by-pass before crashing into the back of us when Reg's brakes failed. With only twenty minutes to go before kick-off we crawled into the Willowmead Stadium, our confidence uncomfortably perched on the gear stick.

Every general has his own method for preparing his troops for battle and I am no exception. No relaxing by the pool or light lunch over *Football Focus* for my lads. No, I tend to break into a crate of Nettles Old Fester.

It was only minutes before the Athletico gladiators took to the field that Chamden's assistant manager, Frank Spanner, announced that owing to an outbreak of foot and mouth amongst the first team, they had been forced to include six second-team men in their squad at Billington Euphonia. This left only five players to face us. Despite pleas from both Spanner and the referee I insisted that the match go ahead, pointing out that not only a principle but also three certain points were at stake.

Before a morose crowd limply reaching double figures battle commenced at three o'clock. With regular centre-forward Kelvin Simple taking over duties in goal, the City Reserves had only four players left on the park. They noted with fear Terry Wade's eight goals within a minute and it was lucky for them the referee had not kicked off before he scored them. Taking my place on the touchline, I noticed as we kicked off the reassuring sight of Ken Mentle in the grandstand giving me the thumbs up before disappearing through his tip-up seat.

As soon as 'Jock' McDougall sent a blistering back pass

crashing against his own crossbar in the first minute, I knew there were only two teams in it. Chamden performed like men possessed and even had the audacity to mount wave after wave of attacks. An uncharacteristic hard tackle by Darren Twink sent a Chamden defender writhing in agony and my hopes soared in expectation of their side being further depleted. 'Twinky', however, without question the fairest and most sporting player ever to don an Athletico shirt, was full of remorse and insisted that the referee, who had not even blown for a foul, send him off. Running on to the pitch I attempted to dissuade Twink, but he remained distraught and adamant. Seeing that no serious injury had been done to the Chamden player, Darren settled on grabbing the referee's notebook and booking himself.

As half-time approached and with the score at 0–0, Reg and I shuffled nervously on the bench, but the duck was about to be broken. Chamden full-back, Vernon Maradonna, intercepted a pass between Doyle and Proby and, with the rest of the Athletico defence sharing a cigarette on the touchline, and John Slack reading *War and Peace* behind his goal, slotted the ball home to give the Reserves a half-time lead.

I entered the dressing room like Atilla entered Rome, by flushing all the oranges down the lavatory. The situation called for some drastic action and so I laid it on the line; either they won this game or I would resign. It was not until the cheers had subsided and Reg Pybus had pointed out the rashness of my statement that I decided instead on getting the match abandoned. Confronting the referee over his mug of vodka, I insisted that he call the game off as it was obvious the five Chamden lads were at a complete disadvantage against our full team. He, however, disagreed and despite my threat to take the matter to the County FA, Lancaster Gate and Esther Rantzen, he decided to carry on.

I then produced a master stroke. I suppose it was just my managerial instinct coming to the fore, but I decided to make a tactical substitution. I pulled off my entire six-man defence and, much to his surprise, sent on Reg Pybus as the lone forward and moved the forwards back into defence.

No sooner had I retaken my touchline seat than Reg, a mile off-side and with the referee unsighted, had hammered home the equaliser. Unfortunately, leaping from my seat in the dug-out, I cracked my skull on its roof and the world turned black.

I eventually came round in the Chamden General Hospital and on the slab next to me was club chairman, Ken Mentle, an oxygen pump beside him, a nurse frantically thumping his chest and Ken rambling deliriously about a Micky Deere scorcher from the penalty spot which had given us victory.

The only sad note was that I missed the second half and was given no credit for our victory, despite masterminding the whole tactical approach to the game. As I told the *Whaddon and Mitchley Argus* and the 'Sporting Mauve', the game went precisely to plan, yet they claimed we were totally out-played and only secured victory because by the last quarter the 'five Chamden heroes' were completely knackered.

LES IN CONFIDENCE

WEDNESDAY, 3rd FEBRUARY

A knock at the door this morning turned out to be a young girl in floods of tears, asking for me. At first I thought it was something to do with Chester, you hear so many disgusting stories about Tech. colleges these days, but then I realised that he would not be interested in a girl unless she had cantilever overhangs and could be seen five miles away from the top of a bus. As it turned out she was Royston Marley's girlfriend, who told me he had been taken away by the police and was being deported. His last words, she said, as he was driven away, were for me. He wanted to thank me for having such an undying belief in his footballing ability and for working tirelessly to further his career in soccer. She told me that he just had time to wrap a small gift of appreciation. In a flood of tears, some my own, she presented me with four frozen chicken portions.

Brilliant! How many ruddy goals am I going to get from a frozzled chicken bit! Actually, a damn sight more than from that stiff gherkin Smott. Hells bells, I should never have quit abstinence. If this is the sort of crap I sign when I am canned I really must try and get back on the wagon.

Watching Smotty's four-minute debut — missing an open goal whilst tying his bootlace, refusing to take a second-minute penalty until he had washed his shin pads in the puddle on the centre circle, then when he did take it hitting the corner flag — I could feel the supporters forcing my head further and further down on the block. I don't know which was more humiliating, that git's performance, or the ape-like dance and inane grinning of Reg Pybus when I pulled him off.

My other 'new boys' were just as dire. Romerez was pathetic and his interpretation of the new 'no passing back to the goalkeeper' rule was bloody unique. I have never seen a player catch a football in his mouth and spit it back to his keeper before. Still, he didn't have to spoil his debut by insisting he left the game ten minutes before the interval so he could prepare his half-time pizza slices.

I did not dare risk Pollock and young Duncan Pugh and so I left them firmly on the bench. Even that did not stop Pugh getting quizzical looks from the referee who asked about his age, so I told him that he was not the Pugh named as sub in the programme but the club mascot.

As results get worse, I still manage to bluff the board into believing I have a long-term strategy that will see us pulling away from the bottom within weeks. I don't have a plan, all I have is a well thumbed copy of *The Alex Ferguson Book of Footballing Euphemisms*.

Rumours continue in the supporters' club, and the Trevor Howard Theme Bar of the Duck and Forceps, that the Singh brothers have earmarked 'The Tip' for re-development. Personally I think it is a load of rubbish. Who would want to build on that bog? As I told a couple of surveyors I met at the ground earlier today, 'Building on here would be like trying to wallpaper a Slumberland mattress.'

ATHLETICO WHADDON

M/SV. DIVISION 3

TODAY

·V·

SPORTING HYDRA CHEMICALS

£1

* OFFICIAL PROGRAMME *

	P	W	D	L	PTS
CLANSFORD UTD	20	13	4	3	43
GOSLING CELTIC	20	11	5	4	38
NORTHTOWN	20	9	5	6	32
SCRIMLEY ARSENAL	20	9	5	6	32
ALBORNE	20	8	7	5	31
FRAMPTON ROVERS	20	8	5	7	29
REDLAND PARK AVENUE	20	7	7	6	28
HELLINGBOROUGH	20	8	3	9	27
SPORTING HYDRA CHEMICALS	20	7	6	7	27
TWITCHIT ALBION	20	7	4	9	25
DORNING TOWN	19	6	7	6	25
LEECH TOWN	20	6	7	7	25
CHAMDEN CITY RESERVES	20	6	6	8	24
FELTON	19	6	4	9	22
BOTHAM WDRS	20	6	3	11	21
SIDCOMBE	20	4	6	10	18
ATH. WHADDON	18	4	1	13	13

MANAGER'S NOTES

20th February '93

During half-time today a number of police officers will be questioning you all over the disappearance, during the early hours of Monday morning, of our grandstand.

The 'Bog Hole', as we affectionately knew it, recently renamed the Ken Mentle Memorial Stand, mysteriously vanished overnight and its whereabouts are still unknown. Besides being the only decent covered area at 'The Tip', the stand was a local landmark, and although not in the same class perhaps as the Eiffel Tower, it was held in great affection by nearby residents. The effort involved in removing it is totally out of proportion with the financial gain anyone could hope to recoup from its sale as scrap metal and firewood. There is no logical explanation for the theft. GIVE OUR STAND BACK.

Have you seen our stand? Keep 'em peeled

*   *   *   *   *   *   *

On the field a fortnight ago we unfortunately caught Frampton Rovers on a good day as they ran out 5–1 victors. However, it was encouraging to see Wayne Pollock get on the score sheet in his debut match with a goal off the back of his head as he stood watching a flock of swans fly overhead. Also encouraging was the performance of Trevor Proby in failing to get his name taken or sent off. This is all the more remarkable as he was responsible for giving away all five penalties. WELL DONE, TREV!

*   *   *   *   *   *   *

Once again I have attracted the wrath of many supporters who think they know more about football than the eleven 'Stiffs' they profess to follow. This may well be so, but I get very tired when they attempt to banter tactics with me.

My appointment as team manager was a radical move on the board's part and my policies must reflect their cavalier approach. Many people were outraged when I lined up a side with ten forwards in our cup game with Hatton Matadors, but remember we came back from 7–0 down. True, we still lost, 7–2, but that is what experimentation is all about.

Football is all about outwitting your opponents, never playing to a formula and always having a change of underwear. It is only through my imaginative shuffling of the aces that we are able to stay ahead of the pack. In the words of John Motson, 'No footballer is an island.' Well, no manager is an isthmus.

*   *   *   *   *   *   *

Those of you who are still concerned about our results should take comfort in the fact that these are early days and with the season barely three-quarters over we still have ten games remaining in which to pull away from the bottom. Should the unthinkable occur, a bottom three position, it should be remembered that we cannot be relegated from the Third Division. As there is no Fourth Division, it would mean playing ourselves every week.

YOUR LINE TO LES

Dear Mr Bence,

So you want me to be constructive, eh, Les? Well, all right.

Look, in my day, before the war, we always had wingers, none of this booting up the middle and hoping for the best. If we had some wingers, Les, I tell you we'd create havoc with our crosses.

Noughts mean 0, crosses mean goals, that's how I see it.

Back in my day we often used to have five or six wingers on the field at once. Course, the ball never left the centre spot because they were all hugging the touchline and refused to get it, but you ask any of the 'old timers' and they will tell you straight, Les, bring back the wingers!

No offence,
G.P.

Dear G.P.,

Thank you for your suggestion. Kicking the ball up field and 'hoping for the best', as you put it, is fundamental to my strategy this season and a change in policy now would only disrupt the well-oiled machine I have created.

The winger belongs to football's more flamboyant age, when players were given free rein on the field and the managers' instructions were nothing more than, 'Get out there and earn your ten bob.' Today a player is simply a pawn, part of a highly organised unit working to a manager's predetermined set of tactics. In our case, this is kick and rush.

Today, primitive skill on the field has been replaced by brains on the bench and, as such, football is now on an intellectual par with chess and skittles.

No offence,
Les.

Bency,

Until we discovered your football club, Saturday afternoons for me and my mates meant spraying rude words on the side of the Co-op or hijacking shopping trolleys.

'The Tip' has given a new meaning to the weekend. No doubt you have spotted the 'Proby Pack', as we call ourselves, clustered at the Sewage Lane end, our shaven heads painted with such menacing slogans as 'Cut out the long balls' or, on a couple of big heads, 'Using two sweepers is a tactical error, Les'.

The thing is, boss, we still think something is missing at the club. Where's the aggro? Nobody wants to fight and the police only make arrests if we telephone them ourselves to report trouble. Every club worth its salt has a hooligan element, so what has happened to ours?

Steve 'The Razor'

Dear Razor,

I cannot condone violence outside of the Oliver Reed Cellar Bar at the Duck and Forceps, certainly not here at 'The Tip' where we pride ourselves on our family atmosphere.

Les

Dear Mr Manager,

I am a young lad of eighteen who has been approached by your official, Mr Reg Pybus, with an invitation to join your club as a player. Although I say so myself, I am not without skill, having represented the county at schoolboy level. I would certainly jump at the chance of a career in football.

There is, however, a problem. I do not drink. Friends tell me that this could seriously hamper my chances of joining Athletico, as it is rumoured your club is just an excuse for getting smashed four or five times a week. Please advise.

Yours,
K.T.

Dear K.T.,

How refreshing to hear of a young lad whose only vice is to want a career in football. Unfortunately, socialising is a vital ingredient when one is a member of a team. Remember, in non-League football a player is respected not only for the number of goals he can put away.

L. Bence

Dear Mr Bence,

Your introduction of a letters page to the match programme should be congratulated. I think it was very brave of you, especially as supporters will use it as an opportunity to criticise you and the team publicly.

However, although your replies are often thoughtful and considered, I have detected a worrying trend of late. Like some of your more illustrious colleagues (Ron Atkinson, Graham Taylor, etc.), you have a tendency to say a lot but to say nothing at the same time. Please remember, Mr Bence, that the majority of Athletico supporters are plain ordinary countryfolk, and to us, words and phrases such as 'perspicacious' and 'total player interface' have no meaning at all.

I am convinced that simple answers, in working man's English and full of hard facts (often lacking in your replies), would alleviate the impression many of us hold that you have become a master in the art of waffling.

What we want is down-to-earth accountability, not lots of incomprehensible grand ideas. Sorry about this, Mr Bence, but do you not agree that sometimes your answers are just too vague?

Yours sincerely,
A. J. Vine

Dear Mr Vine,
Possibly.

Cheers,
Les.

Dear Les,

What do you think our chances are in Europe next season?

The England boss is too much of a diplomat and never gives a clue to his plans, but I am sure a no-nonsense chap like you will not fudge the issue.

Yours in anticipation,
J.M.

Dear J.M.,

I have not followed international football for well over twenty years, preferring to concentrate on the bread and butter of non-League soccer, so I have no idea what Alf Ramsey thinks. I can say with confidence, however, that he knows nothing about Athletico Whaddon. Frankly, we would have a mountain to climb to get 'The Stiffs' into Europe, but you never know. If I can build the squad the way I wish and not be forced to part with exceptional talent like Colin Webley, then anything is possible. I am sorry my reply is so brief, but having just cut my thumb I am unable to continue writing.

Yours in antiseptic,
Les Bence

Dear Les,

As you know I am married to Dave Doyle, right back with the club. I am, I think you will agree, 25 years old with a vivacious personality and one hell of a figure. As you have often told me, Leslie, as a wife of a current first-team member, it is my duty to flaunt these qualities whenever possible, for the good of the club. So may I ask you, Leslie, yourself blessed with endless charisma and, may I say, sex appeal, where am I going wrong on the terraces?

Neither slinky dresses nor thigh-throttling jeans and undulating cleavage seem to arouse the slightest passion into those zombies on the terraces. This does nothing for my ego. Can you offer any explanation?

Yours in confidence,
(Name and address supplied)

Dear Zara Doyle,
Believe me, your appearance is noted every home game, especially by your husband, a consequence of which is that his game is suffering. How much more satisfying for your ego if you were to flaunt your assets around C&A on a Saturday afternoon.

I can only suppose the fans ignore you because they are too engrossed in my thought-provoking programme notes.

Yours in hope,
L.B.

SUPPORTERS' CLUB NEWS

Dave Bull, who many of you will know as a fanatical 'Stiff' and athlete in his own right, has been banned from carrying on shot-putt practice in the bar. Last Friday's unfortunate accident left the club with no alternative.

A framed photograph of Jimmy Hill was dislodged behind the bar and fell, shattering bottles and glasses. Barman Mike Wheeler slipped whilst attempting to catch the picture, badly slashing his wrist on the broken glass and at the same time dropping his lighted cigarette into a box of Buxtons Tripe and Strawberry Flavoured Crisps. These then ignited and the flames caught the draperies behind alight.

In an attempt to extinguish the flames, a number of youths broke into the Space Invaders machine, filled their pockets with an estimated £140 worth of ten pence pieces and hurtled the machine at the blaze. Sadly, it failed to smother the flames but travelled on through the window, coming to rest on Mr Singh's Bentley, causing an estimated £567 worth of damage.

Three cheers, then, for club steward, Rolly Hill. Rolly single-handedly attempted to apprehend the youths, put out the fire and administer first aid to barman Wheeler. Luckily the carbon dioxide stopped the bleeding, 1,400 coins smothered the blaze and the three youths were detained by five yards of sticking plaster and a lead poultice.

The aftermath of these events is that the supporters' club now has debts totalling £4,684. Thanks, Dave.

*　　　*　　　*　　　*　　　*　　　*　　　*

This Sunday we will be holding our popular 'Question of Soccer' quiz in the bar. This week Les Bence and two of his squad will take on a team of religious fundamentalists from

the local mosque. During the interval no questions will be
asked.

*　　*　　*　　*　　*　　*　　*

'Going Down, Staying Up, Going Down' is the first Athletico
Whaddon fanzine. It has been put together by a group of
younger supporters, and the first issue comes complete with
a free disabled driver sticker which should make parking at
away games much easier. The magazine costs 20 pence and
supply your own staples.

LES IN CONFIDENCE

THURSDAY, 18th FEBRUARY

The mental strain of football management is phenomenal. What I do not need is to be awoken at 4 a.m. in the depths of winter, forced from my bed and summoned to gawp at an empty space where once a football stand stood.

Since its 'theft' my living room has been under siege from Mark 'The Scoop' Crowe, the *Argus* sports hack. Already Steve Gillery and myself have suffered the humiliation of having to feign tears, whilst pointing at nothing, for the sake of press photographers.

This morning, as I cooked Crowe breakfast, he told me the story had 'national' written all over it. He told me he would be phoning in copy to the *Sun* although, having no sex angle, they might not be interested. I pointed out that the ground was once part of Tip Farm and that on rainy days Bob Crudge still used it for artificial insemination. Therefore, technically somebody had stolen a fertility clinic.

It was decided at the last cash crisis meeting to get rid of the grandstand and claim the insurance, only local radio jockey, Keith Labone, thought there might be some insurance fiddle on the go. Pahdra Singh handled his on-air interview brilliantly, and pointed out to Labone that grandstands are not insured against theft. What that smarmy jock did not know was that a cousin of Proby, who is in insurance, had insured the grandstand disguised as a car — third party fire and theft. I am not sorry to see the stand go because being shabby, leaky at the back, and all but condemned, it was a constant reminder of the team's own position. At lunchtime I called in the Duck and Forceps for pie and chips in the Nanette Newman Brasserie. This was the first time I had dared to show my face in the D and F since our 7–2 drubbing in the Cup. The team have only themselves to blame. Three minutes before kick-off is not the time to stage a dressing room revolt. As usual I had not named my squad so as to keep the opposition guessing — all I had announced was that there would be eleven players in the team. The 'uprising' came from the forwards who moaned that they never had anything to do. I made a few suggestions, creating chances, scoring goals, but it did not get through. In fact, they flatly refused to play unless they could take over in defence. Well, there was nothing for it, I had to lay down the law in no uncertain terms. Luckily the timely intervention of Trevor Proby's left boot into my right ear quickened everyone's resolve to reach a compromise. Reluctantly I agreed that goalie John Slack should have a ten-man defence in front of him. However, as I had promised attacking football, I named them all as forwards.

Optimism is my middle name because, unable to agree on a name, my parents stuck a pin in a dictionary. But optimistic is also my nature and, although the end of season is in sight, I still believe a final League position of second from bottom is obtainable. At least I will not have to suffer relegation again because the Multivite Vegeburger/Singletons Valve Replacement League Division III is the pits.

Threatening phone bills are quite common in this house, but in the last few days abusive calls have become popular, with an unknown voice offering to dismember certain of my vital organs unless I quit the manager's job. My suspicion first fell on Reg Pybus, but I am now certain it is Howard Wilkinson, seeking some perverted pleasure to compensate for his monumental gaff in signing that prat Colin Webley.

ATHLETICO WHADDON

M/SV. DIVISION 3.

TODAY
· V ·
NORTHTOWN

£1

* OFFICIAL PROGRAMME *

	P	W	D	L	PTS
CLANSFORD UTD	21	13	4	4	43
GOSLING CELTIC	21	12	5	4	41
NORTHTOWN	21	10	5	6	35
ALBORNE	21	9	7	5	34
SCRIMLEY ARSENAL	21	9	6	6	33
FRAMPTON ROVERS	21	8	6	7	30
REDLAND PARK AVENUE	21	7	8	6	29
TWITCHIT ALBION	21	8	4	9	28
HELLINGBOROUGH	21	8	4	9	28
SPORTING HYDRA CHEMICALS	21	7	7	7	28
DORNING TOWN	20	6	7	7	25
LEECH TOWN	21	6	7	8	25
FELTON	20	7	4	9	25
CHAMDEN CITY RESERVES	21	6	7	8	25
BOTHAM WDRS	21	6	3	12	21
SIDCOMBE	21	4	7	10	19
ATH. WHADDON	19	4	1	14	13

MANAGER'S NOTES

27th February '93

Incompetence has, I fear, reached epidemic proportions of late in our local police force. I can only assume this is the reason they have failed to make any progress in hunting down our missing grandstand. I have myself spent many hours at the police station compiling an accurate photo-fit of the stand and, through my many contacts in the local underworld, supplied them with the names of many undesirables known to deal in second-hand wood.

Despite this assistance, they insist on concentrating their enquiries around Trevor Proby's new 'rustic' conservatory. In my opinion, they should stop hounding law-abiding citizens and set about catching the obvious culprits, whoever they are.

*   *   *   *   *   *   *

Following my success in transferring Colin Webley to Leeds United, other top clubs are now casting their chequebooks towards the talent I have nurtured here at Athletico. Only the other week, Reg Pybus spotted the chief scout for Scunthorpe United in the crowd. Obviously he did not make himself known so we can only speculate as to who he was watching, but we are all hoping that Trevor Proby will soon get the call.

Likewise, supporters have reported to me that a well known, flamboyant Football League Premier Division chairman has been seen at 'The Tip'. We may assume that he is not spying on players and so must be on the lookout for managerial talent. Should the call come within the next week, I shall be taking out a full-page advert in the *Whaddon and Mitchley Argus* to express my thanks to you all for your support during my short period as manager.

It must be a rare sight, even in this division, for spectators to see the home side knock in eleven goals in one match, but that is what the Alborne supporters witnessed last Tuesday night. It seems ridiculous for me to try and offer excuses why we were so comprehensively beaten, but the fact that we were well below full strength certainly gave Alborne a ten-goal advantage. Romerez, McDougall and Smith all had work commitments, whilst Jason Pratt and Darren Twink were fulfilling their community service orders. With only ten men available I had no choice but to let Clive Smott play the whole ninety minutes, and even club coach and near octogenarian, Reg Pybus, was forced to get out his old boots and wicker shorts.

* * * * * * *

Today we take on Northtown, who beat us 4–2 back in October, thus denting our then red-hot title hopes. Today's game is sure to be a needle match and, with the runners-up spot a distinct possibility for Northtown, the 'Sausage Men' will have a formidable task in trying to take three points from our rock-solid defence.

* * * * * * *

In an effort to boost club funds, a small tent will soon be found on the far side of the ground. This is to be the new club shop where we hope to sell T-shirts, calendars and fluffy bookmarks in the club's colours.

WHAT THE WIVES SAY...

An intimate insight into the lives of Athletico's stars. As told by the ladies who know them best . . . !

TRACY DEERE

My Micky is just a normal human being at home. I know a lot of fans will find that hard to believe. They also think he must be dominant, decisive and virile but he's not, he's just as he is on the field. He has few hobbies outside of football although, even with his eyesight, he does like reading sell-by dates on goods in shops.

CARMEN ROMEREZ

El Bence, I tell you straight. Back home in Barcelona Miguel could not care less about football. The business always come first. People say he only joined your team by mistake because he loves dancing. He asked a customer if there was a flamenco class in Whaddon, he said there was not, but there were twelve ballerinas at 'The Tip'. Miguel, he just loves to dance, he try anything.

TINA MEEK

Phil likes to spend all his free time with our two boys, Reg and Ronnie. They are out most nights visiting a post office somewhere or repossessing cars. But Phil will never miss his football, not even if he has to lie low for a couple of months. I think he goes training because he knows the police can never find an Athletico training session.

He gets so excited on match days he is often up and about by noon. If it is a home match, though, he will usually get up around two-thirty. I tell you there ain't nothing he would not do for that football club. Once he went up to London with Trevor Proby and a crowbar to sort out that Des Lynam geezer.

ALISON McDOUGALL

Most players' wives at Whaddon are like their husbands and could not care less about football, but both Jock and I live and breathe Athletico. I like to 'shoot' every Whaddon game and it is nothing for Jock to spend a whole weekend analysing, in minute detail, every little aspect of his instruction manual in the hope he can learn to operate the video machine.

Because his heart is devoted to the club, it does not mean his attitude and commitment are always on a par with yours, Les. Luckily, I am there to make sure he snaps out of it. When mid-table apathy sets in, I force him to undertake a rigorous training session which I, naturally, oversee. His programme includes hourly cold showers, a diet of raw cabbage and, on match days, he is suspended from the balcony by his feet, whilst I beat some sense into him with a copy of the 'Sporting Mauve'.

CINDY POLLOCK

Even now I can't get used to my Wayne being a famous footballer. I'll never forget when he came home one night a few months ago and said he'd met this old man who could tell fortunes by reading the dregs in the bottom of a beer glass. Well, Wayne is very gullible when he's had a few and when you, Leslie, told him he was going to be a football star, it went to his head and he happily paid you the £10 signing-on fee.

He seems to be enjoying it, but he has a weak chest and really he shouldn't be out on cold winter afternoons. I must say, though, I think it is very good of you, Les, to let him play those frosty games between November and April in his overcoat.

VAL WADE
Don't talk to me about Terry, Les.

SPOTLIGHT ON THE GREAT PLAYERS

BILL DODD (1932–36)

Bill Dodd, club captain in the 1930s, was one of those players who always gave his all for ninety minutes.

Those ninety minutes he played over three seasons had a lingering influence on fellow players and league positions alike. Bill, who rarely played more than five minutes in any game because of a heart condition, was one of that rare breed who made the art of football look deceptively simple.

When he was on the field, chairs were placed at regular intervals along each touchline so that when he made a break on the wing, he had plenty of opportunity to rest before continuing his blistering run.

KEN MENTLE (1936–40)

Younger supporters will remember the late, lamented Ken as our dedicated chairman for over forty years, but as a player he was perhaps the most talented the club has ever produced. Many believe he should have had a career in professional soccer but in those days, as now, top scouts were unaccountably remiss in visiting 'The Tip'. Perhaps Ken's one failing was that he belonged to a breed of footballer who would later include Charlie George, Rodney Marsh and Emlyn Hughes – big heads.

As a captain, Ken, often resembling an unfit Oswald Mosley, would blatantly push his fellow team mates off the ball if they were in a goal-scoring position, and take the glory for himself. In recounting his goal-scoring triumphs, Ken

Mentle had the unique ability to empty the Duck and Forceps in six minutes flat.

John Motson once said 'This man is like a little human dynamo. He may only be 5 ft 4 ins but he is a giant among small players.' He could have been talking about Ken Mentle. Actually, it was Francis Lee.

BERT FUDGE (1936–40)

The legendary Bert Fudge

That great side of the late 1930s, always remembered as 'Mentle's Mediocres', had so many forgotten players that uncovering Bert Fudge ranks as a milestone in twentieth-century archeology.

When it came to football Bert had one thing on his mind, pigeons. Easily distinguishable in his bird-lime-encrusted shirt and shorts, he often had a look in his eye that spoke of clouds and freedom, rather than the shin-splitting hordes bearing down on him in the shape of the Corton Heath Corinthians. During a crucial match v. Royal Artillery Reserves, his flock of pigeons landed on the goal-line, robbing Whaddon of a last-minute winner. Four birds died in the knowledge that they had pulled off one of the best saves ever seen at 'The Tip'.

ROYSTON MARLEY (1992)

If proof were ever needed that I had a gift for spotting talent then my signing of Royston Marley was it.

Sadly, the intricacies of immigration laws and of jealousy at Lancaster Gate means Marley is no longer available to us. Despite his role as a vital link in my wheel, during his short stay with us I worked tirelessly to further his career. Indeed, I informed both Stoke City and Tring United that they were interested in him. However, with a customary lack of vision, Stoke did not even bother to reply.

Royston was one of the best players we have had since the 1930s. Trevor Proby is another, of course, but his notables should not be discussed in polite company.

LES IN CONFIDENCE

WEDNESDAY, 24th FEBRUARY
ASH WEDNESDAY

The grandstand/insurance fiddle has been a complete balls up. Pahdra Singh has told me that although Proby's cousin did manage to register the stand as a car, he did so describing it as a 1964 Skoda with 300,000 miles on the clock. Instead of the eight grand pay-out we had all expected, what we got was seventy quid and nowhere to shelter from the rain.

I have my fingers crossed, but my own finances may be on the up. There seems every possibility that Trev Proby will be sent down in the near future. I must admit, I credited Proby with a bit more sense. Who in their right mind would build a conservatory with Athletico Whaddon FC emblazoned along the side, and have window frames made from wood bearing the words 'Seats 1–10' and 'Ticket holders only'?

No less than three supporters, all before opening time, have told me that they know for certain that a League chairman has been watching me in recent weeks. I have just put together a mail shot which I am sending to all Premier League chairmen. It includes my CV, a forged testimonial from Mike Channon and the offer to work my first season for a ridiculous 70K a year.

Chester so churned my stomach at breakfast this morning I could not face my sausage, egg and Guinness. The reason for such severe indigestion was a deplorable rag called 'Going Down, Staying Up, Going Down'. This, he gleefully informed me, was the official mouthpiece of the fans where supporters took delight in telling management and directors where to get off. To me it looked like four sheets of Kleenex wiped in something unspeakable and stapled as far away from the fold as possible. It said little about the state of football at Athletico, but quite a lot about the lefty, New Age lecturers who encourage students at the Tech. to run up this garbage.

Naturally, in football management you expect ridicule and criticism, and you must always rise above it, especially if it is constructive, but this poor excuse for a handkerchief seems obsessed not with football but with my receding hairline, e.g. the 'Spot The Baldy' competition on page two, and with making juvenile remarks about my beer gut. Football criticism of any kind is meagre (p6–32), and their undying praise for Reg Pybus' five minutes against Alborne is laughable if not libellous. To say I forcibly removed him in a headlock because he was 'In five short minutes, playing himself back into the job of Athletico manager', is not only true but also likely to get this fanzine banned within a fifteen-mile radius of 'The Tip'.

'Jock' McDougall called round with the merchandise for the club shop. Violence, even after a bucketful of wallop, is not in my nature but, after seeing the goods, throats were throttled. Who is going to buy a T-shirt with the words 'Athletico Whaddon' felt-tipped on to a piece of paper, and Blu-tac'd over an Iron Maiden logo? Is it any wonder McDougall is now on loan to Mitchley Infirmary?

ATHLETICO WHADDON

M/SV. DIVISION 3

TODAY
· V ·
CLANSFORD UNITED

£1

✳ OFFICIAL PROGRAMME ✳

	P	W	D	L	PTS
GOSLING CELTIC	23	14	5	4	47
CLANSFORD UTD	23	13	4	6	43
ALBORNE	23	11	7	5	40
NORTHTOWN	23	11	6	6	39
SCRIMLEY ARSENAL	23	9	8	6	35
REDLAND PARK AVENUE	23	8	9	6	33
HELLINGBOROUGH	23	9	5	9	32
SPORTING HYDRA CHEMICALS	23	8	8	7	32
FRAMPTON ROVERS	23	8	7	8	31
FELTON	22	9	4	9	31
TWITCHIT ALBION	23	9	4	10	31
CHAMDEN CITY RESERVES	23	6	9	8	27
DORNING TOWN	22	6	7	9	25
LEECH TOWN	23	6	7	10	25
SIDCOMBE	23	5	8	10	23
BOTHAM WDRS	23	6	3	14	21
ATH. WHADDON	21	4	2	15	14

MANAGER'S NOTES

6th March '93

Well, I hope all those supporters who complained about lack of entertainment and commitment witnessed our last home game with Northtown.

We were 2–0 up at half-time, through two goals by Dave Doyle, and the change round was barely three minutes old when Ubahni Singh, signed seconds before kick-off, netted his first goal for the club. As if this were not enough, the last quarter saw some of the most exciting football I have ever witnessed and certainly vindicated the raising of admission prices by 68 per cent. Down to nine men, our lads deserve the highest praise for a 3–3 draw.

Once again, though, Trevor Proby received his marching orders and I fear we may never see him in a 'Stiffs' shirt again. The club now have no option but to dispense with his services.

I usually have some sympathy for a player who is dismissed simply for being over-aggressive, but I draw the line when this aggro is carried out on a fellow team mate. The deliberate breaking of goalkeeper John Slack's arm by Proby, putting Slack out for the rest of the season, may well sound the death knell for Division Three football at 'The Tip'. Today, all-round utility player, Clive Smott, will wear the keepers' shorts even though Slack is two sizes bigger.

*   *   *   *   *   *   *

Once again my keen eye for spotting talent, where others see only incompetence, has sparkled in bringing Ubahni Singh to the club. A distant nephew of our chairman, 'Hani' is the most exciting prospect I have seen this week. In fact, so impressed am I with his performance that I shall personally be paying his train fare from Birmingham twice a week.

*   *   *   *   *   *   *

As one new face appears another departs. During our game with Sporting Hydra Chemicals in which we trounced them before going down 1–0, Duncan Pugh's false beard came off in a goal-mouth fracas and he was questioned, at length, by referee Bobby Maxwell. The upshot is a fine of £543 for playing an ineligible and non-registered player, and a tearful farewell for Duncan.

*   *   *   *   *   *   *

Finally, may I dispell a couple of nonsensical rumours that are currently circulating. Fans have besieged me of late claiming that in my last programme notes I announced the opening of a club shop. Having read through my notes with a fine toothpick, I can find no mention of the tent on the far side of the ground whatsoever.

News that Mr Pahdra Singh has become an executive with Singh Development Corporation has also started tongues wagging again over the future of 'The Tip'. Let me make it quite clear, Pahdra Singh is committed to this club 116 per cent. To think he would let it fold for the sake of enormous personal gain is, quite frankly, ludicrous. Any fears you may have are, believe me, like Maidstone United, completely groundless.

YOUR LINE TO LES

Ted Cox is almost unique among Athletico supporters as he is one of only a handful who voluntarily attend away games. His presence is much appreciated by the team, and the sight of his moped chained to the grandstand always boosts the team's morale. Below you will find a match report for our thrilling 11–0 defeat at Alborne the other week, which Ted included in a recent letter.

With the 'Stiffs' only able to field ten men, including Reg Pybus, this was always going to be a tough game.

Keith Simmons, Alborne's lethal striker, put them ahead with a goal from the centre spot right on kick-off, and it was immediately obvious that our radical 0–2–7 formation was not going to work. Within another two minutes Simmons was two-thirds towards completing his hat trick after he outpaced all six defenders and side-footed the ball past goalkeeper Slack, who had been caught unawares as at the time he was trying to impress a group of young girls in the crowd by swinging on the crossbar. Undaunted, Athletico played as one man. That man was Reg Pybus. Reg looked at least three divisions better than anyone else on the park, and many of us thought it incomprehensible of 'Bencey' to literally drag him off after only five minutes. In a perverse way, losing their best player lifted the 'Stiffs' and they came more into the game, although Micky Deere and Terry Wade were both booked for negative play. However, failing to operate a successful offside trap, the Whaddon defence saw Combes walk in goal number three.

Simmons dispossessed Meek from the restart and, as he did with his first goal, secured his hat trick by scoring from the centre spot. On the stroke of half-time, Alborne's one-legged defender, Brown, successfully dummied the entire Whaddon back row to give Alborne a 5–0 lead at the interval.

Despite the valiant cries of 'We are the Bencey Boys' from the faithful few, we were subjected to jeers from the Alborne crowd as fighting broke out between the Athletico players on their way back to the dressing room. Order was only restored when manager Bence dowsed them in a bucket of cold Bovril.

The second half began with some of the most remarkable scenes I have ever witnessed at a football match. Within four minutes Simmons had taken his tally to five and an own goal by Smott had given Alborne an insurmountable 8–0 lead. Incredibly, as the game restarted, Phil Meek's boot caught fire. After it was extinguished by ground staff, a furious row then ensued between the referee and our lads. Athletico argued that with so much spontaneous combustion in the air it was dangerous for the game to continue and the referee should abandon it there and then. Mr Bishop was having none of it, however, and the affair turned ugly for a while with the Alborne goalposts being jostled. In a last ditch attempt to save face, I invaded the pitch on my moped but was thrown off, to howls of laughter, when I hit some particularly nasty divots.

As the game got underway again, Athletico launched their only attack which ended in Gillery's shot from three yards clearing the grandstand by over twenty feet. Alborne seemed content to sit on their eight-goal lead but, when four Whaddon players left the pitch with ten minutes to go so they could catch the last bus, it was too good an opportunity to miss, and Alborne finally ran out winners by eleven goals to nil.

TED COX

THE LES BENCE A-Z OF
FOOTBALL, PART ONE

After days of begging from supporters I have at last compiled a comprehensive A-Z of football, Athletico style.

A = ATTACK
Although fans will tell you there is nothing as exciting as attacking football, those who frequent 'The Tip' have probably never witnessed a game between two attacking sides. With every player in the Whaddon team a potential striker, we tend to concentrate on defence but are always ready to spot the half chance to score a breakaway goal. Sometimes we can go five or six games before spotting a half chance.

B = BACK PASS
In the days of forward, Stanley 'own goal' Reynolds, a back pass was always preferable. This tradition of denying our forwards possession continues today. Possession is nine-tenths of the law and the back pass is safe and sure. This season a new law was introduced, evidently, concerning the passing back to goalies. Well, I have not heard anything.

C = COCK UPS
Trying to push Whaddon into the realms of professional soccer means that all my time, twenty-four hours a day, three days a week, is devoted to the team. But as any great manager knows, delegation to those less capable than he can lead to the occasional administrative hiccup. Having said that, doesn't

every club turn up for the wrong match on the right day at least once or twice a season?

D = DEFENSIVE ERRORS
A defence is only as good as its defenders and do not forget that good players do not turn out in non-League football for beer money. In my experience, they are always ruthless, ambitious and dreaming of the lucrative bright lights of Leyton Orient.

E = EVASIVE ACTION
When things are going against him, a manager will often use his cunning to limit the damage. There are a number of ways to get a game abandoned, although streaking across the pitch in only your underpants, as I did at Lake Town last season, is perhaps not the best. Also last season we were due to play Premier Division side Derris Vale in the Cup and doubters said a heavy defeat looked inevitable. However, thanks to my evasive action it did not happen. We failed to turn up.

F = FREE KICK
Apart from a penalty, the free kick is usually a team's best chance of scoring a goal. With an unjustified reputation for less than accurate shooting, our best policy has always been to distract the opposition's concentration on these set pieces. That is why, when we are about to take a free kick, Phil Meek will pull his bottom lip up over his nose and Micky Deere will leap up and down pointing to an imaginary burning Zeppelin.

G = GOALMOUTH INCIDENT

The only one that springs to mind happened at Felton when their goalkeeper and left back got their legs hopelessly tangled and they collapsed in front of Darren Twink who was able to slot the ball home. Unbeknownst to keeper and defender, their laces had been tied together by Sid Dicker, Athletico sponge man and, for this match, replacement linesman.

H = HEADING

Heading for the bar is an integral part of a footballer's social life.

I = INTELLIGENCE

Sadly, as television interviews all too clearly show, most footballers from other teams are monosyllabic in speech and a few yards short of a goal in the brain department. At all levels of the game intelligence is a commodity solely restricted to managers. Two exceptions are Mike Channon and John Motson.

J = JUG LEGS

The late Ken Mentle was reputed to have had such bandy legs, it is said casts were taken by makers of spiral stair rails. His contemporary, Bert Fudge, had knees that pointed precisely east to west, and toes that pointed north to south. He was forced to give up football after stepping on a magnet.

K = KICK-OFF

Every soccer match, from schoolboy level to FA Cup Final at Wembley, starts with a kick-off.

L = LES BENCE

Far-sighted, radical, dedicated. Just three of the qualities I possess that will be invaluable when I get the inevitable call to take up Football League management. As I wander the terraces I often overhear supporters talking about me and the overriding opinion is that 'he won't be here much longer'.

Les Bence. A self portrait in pen and ink

Obviously, you the supporters already accept that I must take the greater challenge when it comes. This is not to say that I will desert the club I love at the first opportunity. No, when I take something on I stick to it, like underpants to a wall.

LES IN CONFIDENCE

WEDNESDAY 3rd MARCH

I hoped a phone call late last night was going to be the chairman of Liverpool offering me the job of manager at Anfield. It turned out to be Terry Wade who had just heard that Trev Proby had been arrested on a number of theft and extortion charges, and had been refused bail. This and our unbelievable performance against Northtown have been the only bright spots in another nightmare week.

Like a twat I decided that attack was the best way of preserving my job, and so I demanded that the board give me complete control over team selection, tactics, welfare etc., with no boardroom interference whatsoever. Surprisingly they agreed and, to show their compliance, said they would leave it up to me to tell Trevor Proby that he was sacked.

Trevor is a man on the fringe of the human race with a very persuasive style, GBH. For the last couple of days I have frantically been trying to work out some sort of compromise, but whichever way I look at it, I just do not have the cash to flee the country. Luckily the police have spared me the ordeal of telling Proby, and also kept my bones intact.

So much for complete bloody control. Pahdra Singh's secretary called earlier to say she would be picking the team for this Saturday's match and that some kid I have never heard of, Ubahni Singh, will be playing centre-forward! Well, no way José was I standing for that. I gave the old bag an ultimatum, either I picked the team or I would quit. She then had the audacity to ask for my resignation in writing. Naturally I withdrew my threat because there is no way I will let Singh and his cronies put one over on Leslie Bence.

There has been a lot of banter in the Supporters' Club lately about the prospect of a supermarket on 'The Tip'. Naturally, those poor, deluded idiots thought that somehow I was in the know as to what was happening. As it brought me an endless supply of free wallop I played along with this. Unfortunately, after the first six or seven freebies things got a little hazy and I understand that I told everyone that Singh and his brothers (no relation) were indeed going to build a superstore on 'The Tip', but that they were also going to spend £2,000,000 on a new stadium for Athletico to be built on top of Mitchley cemetery. Oh, Jesus!

I knew all along of course that Pahdra Singh was only interested in the club for his own profit. You can't pull the bobble hat over my eyes. He knows sod all about football and, talk about stingy, I wish the defence were as tight as the clasp on his wallet. There are, of course, certain charlatans who do receive his grace and favour but, unlike that snake-in-the-grass Pybus, who is always eager to lick Singh's cigar, or smoke his boots, my loyalty cannot be bought. Unless the price is right.

REMEMBER: STOP ACCEPTING DRINKS FROM STRANGERS.

ATHLETICO WHADDON

M/SV. DIVISION 3.

TODAY
· V ·
TWITCHIT ALBION /
DORNING TOWN

£1

✳ OFFICIAL PROGRAMME ✳

	P	W	D	L	PTS
GOSLING CELTIC	24	15	5	4	50
CLANSFORD UTD	24	14	4	6	46
ALBORNE	24	12	7	5	43
NORTHTOWN	24	11	6	7	39
SCRIMLEY ARSENAL	24	10	8	6	38
HELLINGBOROUGH	24	10	5	9	35
TWITCHIT ALBION	24	10	4	10	34
FELTON	23	10	4	9	34
REDLAND PARK AVENUE	24	8	9	7	33
SPORTING HYDRA CHEMICALS	24	8	8	8	32
FRAMPTON ROVERS	24	8	7	9	31
DORNING TOWN	23	7	7	9	28
CHAMDEN CITY RESERVES	24	6	9	9	27
SIDCOMBE	24	6	8	10	26
LEECH TOWN	24	6	7	11	25
BOTHAM WDRS	24	6	3	15	21
ATH. WHADDON	22	4	2	16	14

MANAGER'S NOTES

13th March '93

Today we witness a real feast of football here at 'The Tip' when, due to our forced postponement of home games in late November/early December, we play two games in four hours.

When Dorning Town turned up in December they found no one here. Today, however, not only will they meet forty or less baying Athletico fans but also a team primed for a late surge up the League.

My survival plan spun into action the other week with that hard-fought point against Northtown, and although we went down 4–1 against Clansford United I was not unduly worried – every well-oiled engine needs a little fine tuning. I am sure that today my tinkering with Dave Doyle and Phil Meek's positions will prove too much for Dorning Town and the high-flying Twitchit Albion.

*   *   *   *   *   *   *

Let me apologise for the printing errors that will be found on the team sheets in the middle of today's programme. The team line-ups should read as follows:

DORNING TOWN Macey, Burt, Saliki (P.), Raynes, Moles, Hartley, Chambers, Saliki (H.), Weston, Shaw, Harris. Subs. Wolfe, Prosser.

TWITCHIT ALBION Rodborough, Clout, Pearce, Anderson, Millgate, Tavener, Peterson, Ashbone, Bryant, Noad, Wallis. Subs. Rose, Beef.

You will notice on the printed sheet that Ashbone and Wallis of Twitchit are named as goalkeeper and centre-half for Dorning, and that the Saliki twins of Dorning are named as the Twitchit substitutes. Twitchit's actual substitutes, Rose and Beef, are given as substitutes for Dorning. V. Marlow is not included in either squad despite being named as playing for both Dorning, in place of Hartley, and Twitchit, in place of Millgate. V. Marlow is a figment of the printer's imagination.

*　　*　　*　　*　　*　　*　　*

Luckily I am able to correct these mistakes, which is just as well because we face prosecution from the Trading Standards Office after complaints about our programme for the Clansford clash. To put the record straight, I inadvertently misplaced the team sheet sent by Clansford and, to meet the printer's deadline I was forced to make up their team off the top of my head. Surely no supporter actually believed Bobby Charlton, Justin Fashanu and Tom Finney were turning out for United? Even more remarkable, quite a few of you were certain Mike Channon *did* play. Let me make it quite plain, if Mike Channon ever set foot in the Multivite Vegeburger/Singletons Valve Replacement League Division Three he would not go anywhere but Athletico, even if I had to sell my house and body to keep him here.

*　　*　　*　　*　　*　　*　　*

Finally, following the shock departure of Adie Smith and Jason Pratt (musical differences), we welcome two new faces to the team this afternoon. Kev Knowles has signed from local Jehovah's Witness side Armageddon Wanderers and at his own expense has taken over match programme production, re-naming it the 'Whaddon Watchtower'. Our other new signing is local bricklayer, Billy Lugg. Billy may well be the son of a famous footballer as it has often been rumoured that his mother slept with Plymouth Argyle in the early 1960s.

146

MULTIVITE VEGEBURGER/ SINGLETONS VALVE REPLACEMENT LEAGUE NEWS

For the third time this season, GOSLING CELTIC manager JIM FISH is our 'Manager-of-the-Month'. Jim is now the lucky owner of his third gold spray valve and now has three years' supply of vegetarian burger bites.

*　　　*　　　*　　　*　　　*　　　*　　　*

Mounting debts look certain to close SIDCOMBE FC. Never a great footballing side, if it was not for the fact that they are in the same League as Athletico Whaddon, they would probably be known as the Athletico Whaddon of Division Three. Our legal department will be in touch — LB

*　　　*　　　*　　　*　　　*　　　*　　　*

Strange but true! COLIN STOKES, the SCRIMLEY ARSENAL goalkeeper once owned a dog that only had three legs!

*　　　*　　　*　　　*　　　*

A hilarious incident occurred during LITHERWOOD AND CLEGGS home game against REDLAND PARK AVENUE the other week. A number of L and C supporters, decked out in the team's lime green and guava fruit colours, decided to swop hats with predictably side-splitting results. Some found their new hats too small, others discovered they completely covered their eyes and they were unable to watch the match!

Perhaps we are witnessing a new craze on the terraces to rival the inflatable coffins at ATHLETICO WHADDON.

*　　　*　　　*　　　*　　　*　　　*　　　*

Talking of ATHLETICO, League officials are to investigate claims that the trophy cabinet contains a silver vegeburger inscribed 'Manager-of-the-Year Leslie Bence 1992/1993'. This award has not yet been presented and Mr Bence is not even in the reckoning. When questioned, Mr Bence said he had never seen the trophy cabinet in his life, and was at a loss to explain how it came to be in the director's Portakabin. The League have ordered an inquiry.

*　　　*　　　*　　　*　　　*　　　*　　　*

HELLINGBOROUGH centre-half, JOE STOREY, had an embarrassing time on a recent visit to SCRIMLEY ARSENAL. During the match a three-legged dog ran on to the pitch and devoured Joe's shorts. Wearing the briefest of briefs, red-faced Joe played on until the referee, Mr Jones, very kindly removed his own shorts and lent them to Storey.

*　　　*　　　*　　　*　　　*　　　*　　　*

Works team SPORTING HYDRA CHEMICALS have a new manager in Alf Busby. Although in his new post for less than a month, Alf has made such an impression at Polypropylene Park that throughout the League his team are already being nicknamed 'Busby's Test Tube Babes'.

*　　　*　　　*　　　*　　　*　　　*　　　*

Strange but true! After telling ATHLETICO WHADDON goalkeeper, JOHN SLACK, of his Scrimley counterpart's three-legged dog, John informed me that he can top this. He has a dog with four legs.

*　　　*　　　*　　　*　　　*　　　*　　　*

Struggling BOTHAM WANDERERS have called in the police to help in the search for their forward line. A wag in the crowd quipped that it is so long since they have been in evidence, police enquiries are being hampered because no one can name or describe them.

*　　　*　　　*　　　*　　　*　　　*　　　*

I doubt if MICKEY BROWN will forget his trip to CLANSFORD UNITED in a hurry. During the game the FRAMPTON ROVERS full back heard over the tannoy that his wife had given birth to a healthy baby boy. Mickey was so delighted that he promptly scored a hat trick in his side's 4–1 win. But his good fortune did not stop there. On leaving the field, Mickey found a purse containing four pounds, a pension book and a set of house keys. He immediately set off to hand the purse and its contents into the Clansford club office and there he found a distressed but very grateful Mrs Edie Moon (82), Clansford's oldest supporter. What Mickey did not know was that Mrs Moon was so concerned about the loss of her pension book that she had offered £1,000,000 to anyone who found it! Well, it was certainly Mickey's lucky day.

*　　　*　　　*　　　*　　　*　　　*　　　*

As expected, GOSLING CELTIC's £10,000-rated captain, STEWART TRUCKLE, has turned down a move to Third Division ATHLETICO WHADDON. Stewart told us that Whaddon's offer of a free bus pass and as many pizza slices as he could eat if he signed for the club was 'frankly, insulting'.

THE LES BENCE A-Z OF FOOTBALL, PART TWO

Here is the second half of my exclusive A-Z of football, played the Athletico way.

M = MAN FOR MAN MARKING

When talking about marking players only one man can possibly spring to mind, Trevor Proby. During his career that no-nonsense approach has marked players with seventeen black eyes, thirty-six gashed shins, one bruised toe and a broken arm. He has also concussed two linesmen and shot a dog that once ran on to the pitch at Leech.

N = NONE

As in Alborne eleven, Athletico none. Clutton Town nine, Athletico none, etc. etc.

O = OVER THE HILL

When a manager is faced with no financial resources he has to look for youth or experience to fill out his squad. Many ex-professionals prefer to open pubs or manage Swindon Town rather than to ease themselves into retirement by playing non-League football. Always hopeful, I have in the past approached many players with a view to them joining Athletico. Sir Stanley Matthews, Denis Law and Geoff Hurst are unfortunately still to reply. I have, however, had an encouraging response from Emlyn Hughes.

P = PROMOTION

If we wish to progress up the football ladder, I can only see us doing so by winning promotion. Should we ever achieve this, there are those faint hearts who have unkindly suggested the added attraction of pigs flying over 'The Tip'.

Q = QUEUES

The only queues ever seen at 'The Tip' these days are at the tea counter, where 86-year-old Mrs Scricle attempts to deal with thirsty fans. Mrs S. took over from former club skipper, Colin Webley (has he played for Leeds yet?), and her slowness has already become legendary although, in fairness, she is restricted in her movements by a false hip made of Meccano. She is also known for being frugal and will often only serve visiting supporters after running a used teabag three or four times through a mangle.

R = REFEREE

Those of you who know me well may be surprised to learn that I am not anti-referees. It takes a very special person to be a referee. It takes a moron.

S = SUPPORTERS

In ridding the game of these hangers-on we should perhaps take our lead from cricket, a game nobody watches. By kicking-off on Tuesday mornings at 10.30, and continuing the match for three days, we would clear the terraces of this nuisance. Not only that, but think of the score.

When was the last time Whaddon scored 235 goals and lost?

T = TACTICS

Master administrator, father figure, the last hope for flared trousers, these are but a few of the attributes a manager must possess. But most of all he must be a tactical genius able to out-manoeuvre the opposition at a moment's notice. He should also be an accomplished communicator so that players are able to comprehend complicated positional roto-combinations with defensive and forward deviations outside the norm.

U = UNDERSOIL HEATING

Unbelievably, there are some among us who will stop at nothing to keep a game on. In the past, when a postponement was to our obvious advantage, I have had to physically restrain fanatical supporters from going out in freezing conditions to shovel snow off the pitch. Any supporter doing so is now banned for life.

V = VARICOSE VEINS
With so many 'mature' players playing in the Whaddon strip over the years, varicose veins have often been in evidence. Bob Hanley, who played in the 1950s, had a remarkable 56 and, towards the end of his career, Fred Plumb counted 22 on each leg. Not to be outdone, Dave Doyle claimed to have at least 108, but they washed off in the shower.

W = WHADDON AND MITCHLEY ARGUS
The local rag. The *Argus* should stick to printing what it knows best, like the annual flower show or the quaint old custom of rolling the vicar under a bus. Incredible as it may seem, in Mark Crowe the paper has a sports reporter who is unable to hold his drink.

X = XENOPHOBIA
The list of foreign players attracted to Whaddon over the years has been endless. There have been six – Royston Marley, the four Larson brothers and Miguel Romerez. In these six we have proof that not all inhabitants of Jamaica, Sweden and Spain lack the temperament for this country's robust style of play.

Y = YOUTH TEAM
Being a firm believer in the 'start 'em young' policy but desperate for any player I can get to fill out the first team, I have completely overhauled the youth squad. That is to say I have scrapped it.

Z = ZINGIBERACEAE

Plants belonging to the perennial monocotyledonous family of herbs. (All right, I couldn't think of a footballing Z.)

LES IN CONFIDENCE

WEDNESDAY, 10th MARCH

I have decided that now is the time to get tough. And drink more. Both Adie Smith and Jason Pratt phoned to say they had only just heard we have two games on Saturday. This is, they say, a bit inconvenient as they have to meet their girlfriends in the Charles Hawtrey Patio at the Duck and Forceps at midday. It seems they are then off to Birmingham for a Dire Straits concert. Well, in my book nothing comes before football and so I gave them a simple ultimatum: 'Make your choice. It's skiffle or football.'

We are now two players short and I am going to struggle to find eleven men. There are a couple of possibilities. In the massage parlour at lunchtime, Molly Lugg told me her son was now unemployed because his boss, Trevor Proby, was 'in chains' and she would be grateful if I could find him something to do, as he spends all his time kicking his heels, mostly through shop windows in the High Street. I also had a stroke of luck when a Jehovah's Witness called at the door earlier. He asked me if I was willing to let Jehovah into my life to which I replied, 'Only if he can score goals'. This somehow led to a discussion on local football and I discovered that there were eleven fit men and true down at the Kingdom Hall. Not only did this geezer Kev Knowles agree to turn out for us, he also said he would look after the programme as long as he could incorporate a number of religious tracts.

Having scrabbled round picking up as many 'pros' as I can find, and then weighing them against the 'cons', while looking at everything in the most optimistic light, there can be no doubt that we are doomed. Finishing ankle-high in the League is now a pipedream. The foot, the bottom, the abyss, that beckons for the third consecutive season.

I tried to put some money on the 'Stiffs' finishing bottom with the bookies. I thought if I am going to be out of work, I might as well make some cash out of it. Incredibly, it seems they stopped taking bets on Whaddon finishing bottom way before Christmas.

BASTARDS!

ATHLETICO WHADDON

M/SV. DIVISION 3.

TODAY · V · ALBOURNE

£1

* OFFICIAL PROGRAMME *

	P	W	D	L	PTS
GOSLING CELTIC	26	17	5	4	56
CLANSFORD UTD	26	14	4	8	46
ALBORNE	26	12	7	7	43
SCRIMLEY ARSENAL	26	11	8	7	41
HELLINGBOROUGH	26	12	5	9	41
TWITCHIT ALBION	27	12	4	11	40
NORTHTOWN	26	11	6	9	39
FELTON	25	11	4	10	37
SPORTING HYDRA CHEMICALS	26	9	9	8	36
FRAMPTON ROVERS	26	9	8	9	35
REDLAND PARK AVENUE	26	8	11	7	35
DORNING TOWN	26	8	8	10	32
SIDCOMBE	26	7	9	10	30
LEECH TOWN	26	7	7	12	28
CHAMDEN CITY RESERVES	26	6	9	11	27
BOTHAM WDRS	26	6	3	17	21
ATH. WHADDON	26	5	2	19	17

MANAGER'S NOTES

3rd April '93

The Lord Jehovah be praised! What a day our 'doubleheader' turned out to be. The one score and three who turned up to see the morning game against Dorning had a real treat. An early goal by the visitors made it look as though we were heading for our nineteenth League defeat of the season, but thanks to my inspirational coaching from the touchline, new boy Kev Knowles levelled the score on the stroke of half-time. With their chins dropping to their shorts, Dorning were unable to match the flair and fitness of a rampant Athletico and Darren Twink's winner, headed in off his new bouffant hairdo, is my choice for 'Goal-of-the-Year'. Sadly, it was inevitable that we could not keep up the pace against Twitchit Albion, especially with so many of our squad approaching the twilight of their careers. The club doctor was a constant fixture on the pitch, applying oxygen and mouth-to-mouth resuscitation. In the circumstances, a 9–0 defeat shows that ordinarily there would be nothing between the teams.

*   *   *   *   *   *   *

No doubt you are all aware of the County FA's decision to relegate the bottom club in Division Three after all. The unfortunate club will drop into a local Sunday League. Although it is early days yet, should we be that club, then it can only spell disaster. The loss of our semi-professional status would bring about a mass exodus of players as many of them rely on their match fees to bolster dole cheques. My own position would also be called into question, as I regard Sunday as sacred.

*   *   *   *   *   *   *

After 55 years at 'The Tip', Athletico will be losing their home at the end of the season. Following Mr Singh's purchase of neighbouring land for a supermarket, it has come to my knowledge that, reluctantly, customer car parking facilities demand that he also purchase 'The Tip' for a car park. As Mr Singh somewhat harshly pointed out, a pitch for a team in our position could be nothing short of a liability. I have moved quickly to secure a ground-sharing scheme with the local comprehensive school. They have a fine pitch although there are no floodlights and the pitch will not be available at weekends. I am sure that, like myself, you will be sorry to leave our old home, scene of many moral victories and one or two actual ones over the years.

*   *   *   *   *   *   *

Our recent spate of away games has yielded plenty of goals but not for the 'Stiffs'. Dorning Town were quick to gain revenge for their defeat here a few weeks ago, by overcoming us 4–0. It is worth noting that had they not scored those four goals the game would have been drawn. The lack of a goalkeeper was exposed most harshly at Felton on Saturday. Thankfully their absent-minded forwards kept the score to a respectable 3–1.

These defeats only heighten the fact that victory today is vital. A week is a long time in football, seven days in fact, but somehow a reversal of February's 11–0 defeat at the hands of today's opponents would prove that Lazarus doesn't have the last word in comebacks, and we are still a team to be reckoned with.

As you know, when the chips are down Leslie Bence comes out fighting. At great personal cost to myself I have recruited the much sought-after Felton Rovers reserve keeper, Igor Pushov. Igor is on loan to us today for 37 minutes and, should he keep a clean sheet, I will have no hesitation in offering him a full contract and the captain's job.

Terry Wade, Whaddon's longest serving player, has decided to retire after today's game. At an emotional meeting earlier this week, Terry told me 'I've lost touch with the modern game, Les, nobody seems to be interested in drinking these days, all they want to do is get on with the football.'

I know many of us agree with these sentiments and perhaps envy Terry for getting out now. His team mates have already made a collection for him and twenty Benson and Hedges, plus two old betting slips allegedly once owned by Lou Macari, will be presented to Terry at half-time.

SPOTLIGHT ON GROUNDHOPPING WITH CHESTER BENCE

Besides being the son of Athletico manager Les Bence, Chester is president of the Whaddon Groundhoppers. This dedicated band of three have given over their lives and wallets to visiting every football ground in the Multivite Vegeburger/Singletons Valve Replacement League. In the following article he attempts to convey some of his enthusiasm for his pastime.

*   *   *   *   *   *   *

Many people reckon we are all a bit loony spending all our spare time going round the non-League grounds of the M/SV but I can think of one really good reason for doing it. It is really brill. When I started, I was very much on my own but over the years it has really caught on in Whaddon and now membership has trebled. If YOU have ever thought of joining, then do not hesitate because it is brilliant.

For your £6 subscription per annum, you get a free bus timetable giving you the times of at least three buses that visit no less than eight M/SV clubs. These timetables are the same as those you get free from the depot but the difference is that the club copies are all signed by my dad and so are brilliant. Also you get a special hat to wear. This is conical in shape and worn when you visit a new ground. On the front of the hat is the letter 'D', this stands for 'done it' i.e. visited the ground.

A small identity card is also issued to each member and this is worth the price of subscription alone. By flashing said card at any M/SV official at any ground you will be at liberty to

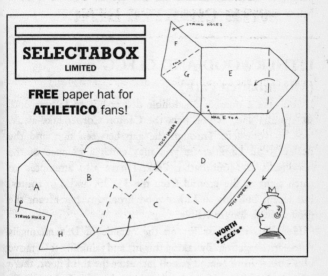

inspect the underside of the grandstand should you be working, as I am, on a survey of all pre-1950 steel structured stands and their method of construction. Similarly, I have found it useful in my research on roof fascia of the Premier Division. In other words, the card is brilliant.

Now if anyone is tempted to join our happy band may I give you some advice which will ensure you get maximum enjoyment from your hobby – specialise. Apart from my own field already mentioned above, others may choose to research Victorian turnstiles, pre-war floodlighting, tea hut menus or programme design; then again, there is still much work to be done on Second Division lavatories. One of our members, my best mate Steve Frost, has a really brilliant speciality which means he never actually visits grounds at all. 'Ground Reconnaissance From Public Transport' is the title of the pamphlet he produced for our last AGM. I quote from it below because it is brilliant.

*　　　*　　　*　　　*　　　*　　　*　　　*

LITHERWOOD AND CLEGG
(Mountbatten Park)

If you take a number 36 double decker bus to Litherwood, sit upstairs and, as you pass the Canton Corner take-away, look to your left. Through the gap between that and the Bezley Road Launderette you may catch a glimpse of the floodlights at Mountbatten Park. I have also attempted to catch sight of the ground from the 31, 29, and 37b routes, but recent building in Litherwood Broadway has meant the ground is no longer visible.

However, the glass lift on the outside of Debenhams is worth investigating. By taking this lift and jamming it (remove blue circuit from behind panel) just after the third floor, there is a good photo opportunity with a glimpse of the cheeky little pink cantilever stand.

BORUSSIA MUNCHEN URCHFONT
SPORTS AND SOCIAL UNITED
(The Welfare Field)

Those of you who jet off to foreign parts for your hols and fly from Chamden airport, may be interested to know that your flight path probably heads out over The Welfare Field.

On a charter flight to Spain last year I spotted the club's ground as we climbed. If I had so wished, I could have climbed out on to the wing and with the use of a telephoto got an unusual shot of the unique S-shaped ground with its mock-Wembley turrets in terracotta. Such a photograph would rank alongside my snap of Heaven Oak Corinthians Musseldyke ground director's car park, taken from a rapidly descending hot air balloon.

THINGLEY BOROUGH VISIGOTHS (Greenwood Lane), FRAMPTON ROVERS (Happy Shopper Leisurerama), CORAN BROTHERS ELECTRIC AND WIRELESS (Linekar Avenue)

By catching the Chamden-London Inter-City train it is possible to go from the Second Division to the Third and back again on this unequalled trip.

As you pull out of Thingley station this otherwise boring train ride takes on a whole new significance. On crossing the viaduct look north-east towards HM Prison – the Greenwood Lane floodlights are clearly visible for at least 45 seconds. Then, as the train follows the curve of the track, over the top of Nettles brewery you can see, by swinging from the luggage rack, all four gantries.

Passing through Frampton only someone on a completely different train on a completely different line could fail to see Rovers' ground in the Happy Shopper Leisurerama complex with its 24-foot inflatable baked bean can nestling against the track. If you are unfamiliar with the ground, however, the stadium itself may well pass you by. The latex medieval castling in startling black also doubles as the Frampton grandstand and their artificial pitch (100 per cent concrete) lies below it. Snow White's cottage at the far end is, in actual fact, the club house and the two giant toadstools are the players' dressing rooms.

Coran Brothers FC have their ground on the outskirts of Watley and as the train goes through the middle of the town you may think it impossible to see any of Linekar Avenue but this is not so. As the train slows down considerably on the bend, look out beyond the Castoff Carpet Centre (formerly Watley Baptist Chapel) over the spire of Saint Greavsies and you may be able to spot the rusty corrugated sheeting, glistening muddily in the sunlight, that makes up the ground's perimeter fencing.

*   *   *   *   *   *   *

Copies of Steve's pamphlet and his earlier work, 'Spotting Football Grounds From Tall Buildings A Long Way Off Volume 1', are on sale at the club office, price £1.75. They are both brilliant. As well as Steve's publications our newssheet covers such topics as spotting grounds from branch line trains and local buses, and our most recent sheet contained an article on a spectacular view of Northtown's thatched terraces that can be obtained by skateboarding off the top of the multi-storey on to the roof of Lloyds Bank.

*   *   *   *   *   *   *

So as you can see, studying football grounds is a brilliant hobby. Even 'The Tip' which, I must admit, cannot compare with Sporting Hydra Chemicals' spanking new ground, Polypropylene Park, has enough history to make a visit an absorbing day out.

If it is a pastime with a difference that you are after, then why not take up groundhopping. It is brilliant.

CHESTER BENCE

PLEASE NOTE All groundhoppers are expected to wear the following regulation uniform: 'Donovan' canvas cap, blue anorak with Ford Motors logo, brown Crimplene trousers, a battered Liverpool/Spurs/Hendon hold-all, a dog-eared red 'Winfield' notebook with short two-inch pencil, filthy trainers, a hideously expensive camera and a pocket full of Mars bars.

LES IN CONFIDENCE

THURSDAY, 1st APRIL
APRIL FOOLS DAY

Gerry Wills, the Frampton Rovers manager, gave me a ring to say that he had a proposition that may well be to Athletico's advantage. Intrigued, I invited him over and he told me that he was interested in the 'leg-over' possibilities of my back bedroom. It seems he is indulging in some extra physio with the little darling who runs on with the sponge for Frampton. She is insisting that Gerry finds them a 'love nest' a safe distance from his wife. Getting his drift, I willingly agreed as long as he could help me out with my goalkeeper crisis. He did not hesitate in offering me his reserve goalie, the Ukranian, Igor Pushov. 'Iggy' it seems had not settled at Frampton mainly because he did not speak English. Frankly, this surprised me, for as I told Gerry, 'an inability to speak English never hampered Ian St John's football career.' Gerry pointed out, however, that referees were not happy having Pushov and his interpreter stood on the goal line as it gave us an unfair advantage. Agreeing to the deal, I will vacate my pad every Monday evening and every third Sunday.

With the threat of relegation looming again, the loss of the ground, and the millstone around my neck of a team of asthmatic pine martens with the collective brain power of a kiwi fruit, the pressures on me are building to a frightening pitch. The Samaritans have threatened to call in the police if I do not stop pestering them with phone calls, and Alcoholics Anonymous refuse to come out for a drink and discuss my problem.

The Singhs' supermarket swindle has at least got

them out of my bald patch, as the prospect of lots of money has put football right out of their heads. Reg Pybus, with his gun at my head, is always ready to stab me in the back though, and eighteen unlucky defeats has given him plenty of ammunition. I am sure he is the toad behind the unprecedented negative media coverage we are getting at the moment.

My appearance on Radio West's 'Football North' yesterday went well, I thought. It was a stroke of genius on my part to avoid such awkward questions as 'Why has the club such an appalling record?' and 'Is the club's current position due to managerial incompetence?' by pretending it was a terrible phone line and I could not hear the questions. It probably fooled the listeners as only the presenter knew I was actually in the studio.

As for Mark Crowe, the *Argus* sport and nature ramble hack, well, I thought I could expect some loyalty there. His recent article entitled 'Hoof It Bency', apart from being completely devoid of grammar or sentence structure, was one long eulogy in praise of that grass Pybus. Reg used every opportunity to take swipes at me and constantly implied that I had lost the confidence of everybody involved with the club. I telephoned him as soon as I had read the article, and told him that he is facing a very heavy fine for talking to the Press without my permission. Although he pathetically offered me an apology, I remained adamant until we struck a compromise. He told me to get stuffed.

REMEMBER: TELL CHESTER TO GET OUT AND FIND A FLAT BY SUNDAY.

	P	W	D	L	PTS
GOSLING CELTIC	27	18	5	4	59
ALBORNE	27	13	7	7	46
CLANSFORD UTD	27	14	4	9	46
SCRIMLEY ARSENAL	27	11	9	7	42
HELLINGBOROUGH	27	12	6	9	42
NORTHTOWN	27	12	6	9	42
TWITCHIT ALBION	28	12	5	11	41
FELTON	26	11	5	10	38
SPORTING HYDRA CHEMICALS	27	9	10	8	37
FRAMPTON ROVERS	27	9	9	9	36
REDLAND PARK AVENUE	27	8	12	7	36
DORNING TOWN	27	8	9	10	33
SIDCOMBE	27	7	10	10	31
LEECH TOWN	27	7	8	12	29
CHAMDEN CITY RESERVES	27	6	9	12	27
BOTHAM WDRS	27	6	3	18	21
ATH. WHADDON	27	5	2	20	17

MANAGER'S NOTES

10th April '93

Champions 1992/1993 Multivite Vegeburger/Singletons Valve Replacement League Division Three!

Yes, the lads have done it! With four games still to play, the side have clinched the Third Division title and promotion to Division Two.

WELL DONE, GOSLING CELTIC!

We must also extend our congratulations to our neighbours, FC Titford Polymer Converters, for taking the Second Division championship at the first attempt. Being only two miles away, their success has meant that many fair-weather 'Stiffs' supporters have been attracted to their games and in consequence our gate receipts have suffered. Titford have undoubtedly had a great season but I wonder if you have stopped to consider which club has really been the more successful? Benny Polymer, the Titford manager, made it plain at the start of the season that promotion was his goal. Well, he certainly achieved it but remember, winning championships is the easy option. OK, the club benefits in the short term – better gates, better football, bigger income – but that is not how we operate here at Athletico. Neither short- nor long-term success is of any interest to the 'Stiffs', as our record shows.

We are dedicated to experimentation, to pushing back the frontiers of football as we know them, to boldly go where no self-respecting soccer club has gone before, and no, I do not mean the Whaddon and Mitchley Sunday League. Of course paying customers want to see a winning side, and they want superficial honours like League titles and Cup runs, but that is not the Whaddon way. Just look at some of the thought-provoking policies I have introduced this season. By using our budget wisely, I have pioneered the signing of players with obviously limited ability, then groomed these novices, many of whom had never kicked a football before, into first team regulars. I have also advocated holding a bottom three position in the table for as long as possible. Some see this as indicating a constant relegation battle come the winds of March, but I believe it is only from such a lowly position, lulling opponents into a false sense of security, that we can wreak havoc on the rest of the League. The secret of this strategy is, of course, to know when to make that surge up the table before the certainty of relegation sets in. As can be seen from our position at the bottom, it is a secret we have yet to uncover.

*　　　*　　　*　　　*　　　*　　　*

I have been greatly encouraged by our recent form. The unlucky 4–0 defeat at home to Alborne showed great promise for the future and if it had not been a mathematical impossibility since the beginning of October, I would have said that playing like that we should still be promotion contenders.

*　　　*　　　*　　　*　　　*　　　*

The great talking point at the Alborne match was the first appearance in many months of our chairman, Mr Pahdra Singh. Despite some unnecessary barracking from supporters, Mr Singh certainly enjoyed himself and got behind the team. In fact, after going three goals down, in sheer desperation Mr Singh ran on to the field, dispossessed an Alborne forward, rounded two defenders and netted in the top left corner. Although I insisted to the referee that the goal should stand because I had sent Pahdra on as substitute, the ref was not fooled, especially as Mr Singh was still wearing his dufflecoat and brogues. Pahdra was escorted from the pitch by a police poodle. Unfortunately, this so incensed some supporters that an ugly incident occurred which was sensationally reported in the *Whaddon and Mitchley Argus* under the banner headline 'Ref Struck by String'.

* * * * * * *

I hope today that all excitement is centred around the Felton goalmouth. If not, let's hope we can complete the double over them and get the game postponed for the second time.

YOUR LINE TO LES

Dear Les,

A few weeks ago we were fortunate enough to meet in a public house where I bought you half a dozen pints and we engaged in a long and fascinating conversation.

During our discussion, you told me that you were about to leave the manager's job at Athletico and take up a similar position with Ipswich Town. You also told me that for eleven years you were national coach and team manager to the United Arab Emirates. Since our meeting I have read nothing about your appointment at Ipswich and believe they are quite happy with their current manager. Also, my *Vauxhall Opal Mints Directory of World Soccer* does not mention your name as ever being connected with the Arab states. How do you explain yourself?

Yours sincerely,

J.T.

Dear J.T.,

To be honest, I do not recall our conversation, or you.

So many people ply me with drinks in the D and F these days that I tend to remember them as I saw them, in a blur.

The Ipswich job was naturally very hush-hush, so I am unable to go into details until my autobiography is published by HMSO in 1999. As to your other query, there is some confusion here I think. The United Arab Emirates that I coached play in the Holtons Sonic Welding Intermediate League (North) and are not a national side at all.

Les Bence

Dear Mr Bence,
I was astonished, to say the least, the other day when I over-heard you tell my young son and his friend that Mike Chan-non, the former Southampton and England footballer, now turned racing magnate, was your brother-in-law.

Well?

Mrs Y. Lamb,
(In disbelief)

Dear Mrs Lamb,
If I had a pound for every time Mr Channon has tried to cash in on my success, I could launch a takeover bid for Manchester United.

He knows full well that we are not related, though he once waved to me from a passing train. As far as I recall from school biology, you do not acquire relatives by waving.

Yours,
Leslie Bence

SPOTLIGHT ON THE ATHLETICO WHADDON CUP RECORD

If League football is a club's bread and butter, then a good Cup run must be the icing on that bread and butter.

Cup games bring relief from the cut and thrust of the League and more importantly can bring much needed revenue to the club. Unfortunately, with a marginally less successful Cup than League record, Athletico have never been in that position. We have however entered a large number of competitions over the years: the FA Cup, FA Vase, County Shield, Debenhams Floodlit Cup and the Sherpa Tensing Van Trophy to name but a few.

THE COUNTY SHIELD

Despite having come a close second to every junior side in the county at least once over the years, as the senior side in the tournament it is hardly surprising that Athletico should have done remarkably well.

Since the club's formation in the 1930s we have reached the first round on no less than 42 occasions. We have reached the second round seven times and the third once. The fourth, fifth, sixth, quarter-final, semi-final and final have, as yet, eluded us.

FA CUP

The greatest of them all. The FA Cup is every club's dream ticket, whatever their status. At the end of our golden period in the 1930s a 2–0 victory over Ditchford Colliery took us past the Preliminary Preliminary First Qualifying Round, although we faltered in the following Preliminary First Qualifying Round, losing 6–2 to Bonsford Hartley of the South FC.

Uniquely, Athletico have had their number slip beneath the lining of the draw hat on no less than four occasions.

FA TROPHY AND FA VASE

Athletico are eligible for both of these tournaments and alternate between the two, one season the Vase, the next the Trophy. Unfortunately, the club seems incapable of deciding which one it is in at any given time. As you may recall, last season we failed to get our name drawn from the Vase hat and, remembering past FA Cup fiascos, I gave the lads the first round Saturday off. It was only by chance that, walking home from the D and F, I spotted our Northern 'opponents', Bleet Town, sitting bewildered in a deserted 'Tip'. They had arrived to play us in the Trophy. The outcome was a £250 fine and disqualification for two seasons.

DEBENHAMS FLOODLIT CUP

Now three seasons old, Athletico had a surprise 2–1 first round victory over Shedford Sunday in the first year, before going out to Nettles 5× Lager/Kellys Spicy Bacon Bites Division One champions, AFC Brampton by seven goals to less.

Last season, of course, we fancied our chances of reaching the second round quite comfortably as our opening opponents were lowly Hellingborough. During a nail-biting second half, with the score 1–1 to the 'Whads', the floodlight collapsed on to the goalposts. This caused them to sink into the ground until the crossbar was only two inches above the grass. The game was abandoned, Athletico fined £270 and the club was disqualified from the competition for two seasons.

LES IN CONFIDENCE

WEDNESDAY, 7th APRIL

After reading my just completed programme notes for this Saturday, I have decided that spending money on a creative writing course at the Tech. would be a waste of money. I am a natural.

Reluctantly, I attended the celebration at the Docherty Suite, Titford, for Polymers Championship. Although I had a mouthful of sour grapes I thought it was worth going so I could corner Polymers football club chairman, Stan Bates. Having received no reply from Wrexham to my offer of taking over as manager, I have decided to set my sights a little lower, hence my chat with Stan. I told Bates straight out that I was the only man who had the vision and know-how to keep his club in the First Division and that for a reasonable salary, say 15K a year, I would be willing to quit Athletico. Naturally I approached Bates in the strictest confidence, but all too quickly I learned that he is just a gin-sodden loud-mouth. Within minutes my offer was all over the Docherty Suite, and I became the source of hysterical laughter, ridicule and abuse. Humiliated, I made my excuses – dinner with Mike Channon – and left.

On returning home I retired, tucking myself up in bed with a hot toddy bottle. I had not been counting own goals for more than a few minutes when I heard extraordinary sounds coming from my wardrobe. Switching on my bedside lamp, I picked up a heavy, blunt instrument (*The Rothmans Football Yearbook 1986/87*) and tore open the door. There, crouching among my nylon shirts and 'World Cup Willy' T-shirt collection were Mark Crowe and an *Argus* photographer.

Crowe offered a pathetic excuse about investigating woodworm infestation for his nature column, but I soon beetled the truth out of him. He told me that in my back bedroom was a sensational sports story of sex, drugs and liniment. He believed an, as yet unidentifiable, soccer manager was using my house for adulterous purposes with a young female on his staff. Naturally, I told him his suspicions were preposterous and, even if they were true, I would never betray a fellow professional. Crowe then had the vulgar audacity to offer me a pitiful ten quid if I revealed the manager's name. I viewed his offer with utter contempt and told him 'Gerry Wills, Frampton Rovers'.

The arrogance of some of the has-beens in the Athletico squad is pathetic. This week alone, Twink, Doyle, Pollock, Smott and Deere have all said they will not be playing for the 'Stiffs' next season as they are TOO GOOD for Sunday League football! Well, if they think they are going to follow me into the Multivite/Singletons First Division when I take over at Titford Polymers, then they are going to be bloody disappointed.

ATHLETICO ·WHADDON

M/SV. DIVISION 3

TODAY · V · LEECH TOWN

£1

✳ OFFICIAL PROGRAMME ✳

	P	W	D	L	PTS
GOSLING CELTIC	29	20	5	4	65
ALBORNE	29	14	8	7	50
CLANSFORD UTD	29	15	4	10	49
HELLINGBOROUGH	29	13	7	9	46
NORTHTOWN	29	13	6	10	45
SCRIMLEY ARSENAL	29	11	9	9	42
TWITCHIT ALBION	30	12	6	12	42
SPORTING HYDRA CHEMICALS	29	10	11	8	41
REDLAND PARK AVENUE	29	9	12	8	39
FELTON	28	11	6	11	39
DORNING TOWN	29	9	10	10	37
FRAMPTON ROVERS	29	9	9	11	36
SIDCOMBE	29	8	11	10	35
LEECH TOWN	29	8	8	13	32
CHAMDEN CITY RESERVES	29	7	10	12	31
BOTHAM WDRS	29	6	3	20	21
ATH. WHADDON	29	6	2	21	20

MANAGER'S NOTES

17th April '93

What a week! I have always said football is unpredictable unless you know what is going to happen.

Last weekend we were caught in a fierce struggle with Felton. A minute to go, 1–1, Meek netting in the first half, when an open goal stares Darren Twink in the face. His shot hits the corner flag, rebounds on to the crossbar and 'Twinky' is there to smash home the winner with his tummy. ATHLETICO 2, FELTON 1! The score was even more remarkable because we played well below our best. As you know, I am a manager who has never shirked from putting a player's welfare before football and, unlike many less tolerant managers, I was quite happy for Steve Gillery to hold his stag 'night' at 10 a.m. on the morning of the match, albeit a game crucial to our survival. Unfortunately, although a good time was had by all, a number of the team picked up a strange flu bug. Black coffee and treacle soup flowed in abundance before kick-off but a number of players obviously played with extremely high temperatures. This explains our erratic performance and the peculiar antics of Steve Gillery who insisted on wearing his shorts on his head, and 'Mig' Romerez who was booked for kissing a linesman. Luckily, Felton were at full strength, so we had little chance of losing.

*   *   *   *   *   *   *

Following Botham Wanderers' defeat, we now move off the bottom for the first time in four months. The victory over Felton certainly got the 'Stiffs' buzzing at Sporting Hydra Chemicals on Tuesday night but, sadly, we failed to respond to their 5–0 half-time lead. I had pulled the team together by the second half, and Sporting found us a very different proposition and were lucky to hold us to 0–0. In fact, if they had not scored those early five goals they would not have won.

We should, of course, be going into today's game with Leech Town knowing that only a victory will keep us in the League. THIS IS NOT SO. I can now reveal that if we remain second from bottom we will not be relegated. This is all due to Sidcombe having resigned from the League. We do not, of course, wish to gloat, having come close to liquidation many times ourselves, but it has to be said, WELL DONE, SIDCOMBE!

*　　　*　　　*　　　*　　　*　　　*　　　*

As you are no doubt aware, a new League ruling states that a point will be deducted for every ineligible player a club fields. Not wishing to take chances at this critical time in the season, I have had to drop four regulars from the side today. This makes team selection difficult and the problem has been heightened by my sacking of club coach, Reg Pybus. Reg gave his life and soul to this club, plus an extra 110 per cent per match, but unfortunately he chose to undermine my authority in such a way that I was forced to demand his dismissal by the board.

Rumours will no doubt circulate throughout the town and, as a figure of authority within the club, I am sure the artisans on the terraces will side with Reg, but let me put forward my reason for sacking him. Without my knowledge or authorisation, Reg took it upon himself to hand the Press a list of star names I was proposing to bring to the club. He suggested that should these signings go through, the club would be plunged into bankruptcy. The local gutter press, the *Whaddon and Mitchley Argus*, then printed the following names of players I hoped to sign – C. Flower, Tom Atoes and a mysterious Russian, Ham Tinof. This action of Reg's was totally irresponsible on two counts. Firstly, I have been in football management long enough to know that team changes at this late stage will do nothing for the confidence of existing players. Secondly, what he actually published was my supermarket shopping list. I know back in the 1930s Bradford City had a full back called McLuggage, but surely not even Reg believes that somewhere out there is a left back called Halfpound O'Liver.

*　　　*　　　*　　　*　　　*　　　*　　　*

May I urge you all to generously support today's raffle. In all my years at the club I cannot remember such a sensational line up of prizes as are on offer here.

FIRST PRIZE A chicken egg.
SECOND PRIZE Four cooking apples.
THIRD PRIZE A box of matches (minimum contents 65).

PHEW!

TRY
Greavsie's
PORK PIES

"they're evil!"
SAYS RESERVE **ATHLETICO**
STRIKER *Gummy Wood*

RUBBER PASTRY * ADDED 'E'
NUMBERS * FINEST OFFAL

SUPPORTERS' CLUB NEWS

Despite an increase in attendance this year, our annual club dinner last Friday evening was a very mixed affair.

Mrs Mentle, the widow of her late husband, gave a short introductory speech in praise of him and his achievements for the club. A number of younger members present, already the worse for drink, interrupted her speech on a number of occasions as they chanted 'Bring on the stripper' and 'Let's get inflation down to nought per cent'. Obviously distressed, Mrs Mentle cut short her speech and forgot to present the 'Player-of-the-Year' award. In fact, no player received the required three votes to qualify and in the players' 'Player-of-the-Year' award each player voted for himself. However, 160 supporters voted for Trevor Proby, but as he is no longer a member of the club those votes were declared void.

The meal then followed and all had their fill of sausage rolls and crisps, washed down with delicious barley water. A number of guests, unaccustomed to attending formal functions, caused a few unpleasant moments when they began targeting abuse at social secretary, the Reverend Shrigley. The main substance to their complaints was that at £26 a ticket they were not receiving value for money. The good 'Rev.' attempted to pacify them by pointing out that the evening was a glorious opportunity to meet the players in an informal atmosphere, and to buy their heroes a drink. This only seemed to exasperate the situation and it was some time before order was restored.

Supporters' Club member, Jack Mattock, then presented a slide show entitled 'My Favourite Ferrets'. Jack, who has been breeding ferrets for more than forty years, showed us soft focus shots of brown ferrets, white ferrets, ferrets eating mice

187

and ferrets building their nests in old Athletico programmes. His thirty-minute ramble was greatly appreciated by all present, as it enabled many to sleep off their pre-meal excess of Nettles. Regrettably, it also gave those 'Bog End' supporters present a chance to run loudly through their repertoire of football chants and sea shanties.

The main event of the evening was a speech by Mr Leslie M. Bence, currently team manager. A number of guests and most players left at this point and so missed the 'Boss' deliver a riveting talk entitled 'Taylor, Channon and Bence'.

Les had us all on the edge of our seats and those who remained found their voices again, encouraging Les with a deafening cry of 'Bring back the ferrets'. The climax came when a show of hands was asked for to vote on a proposal that the evening's raffle prize, a cuddly soap dish, be replaced by the manager's job. When the motion was carried, bottles and fists began to fly and unfortunately Mr Bence was ejected when the police had to be called.

Those remaining then went home after the Queen. (The anthem that is, not Her Majesty, who failed to reply to our invitation to deliver the Ken Mentle Memorial Lecture.)

*　　　*　　　*　　　*　　　*　　　*　　　*

Jones and Pratley, the motor coach company, have told Supporters' Club officials that they will no longer be able to hire their coaches for away games. A service bus, number 58, will get you to Gosling for our last away match of the season. There are two buses a day from Whaddon which leave outside the nuclear shelter at 6.15 a.m. or 7.34 p.m. The only return bus (Gosling-Whaddon) leaves at midday. Next season, the Supporters' Club hope to start up a bicycle hire scheme for away matches. This will include special six-seater machines for those who like to travel in organised gangs.

LES IN CONFIDENCE

WEDNESDAY, 14th APRIL

Things started so well at the weekend I knew it could not last. The win over Felton still hasn't sunk in. All I can say is, it is a good job players are not breathalysed before a match, because all of us were completely smashed! Thanks to the rank stupidity of Steve Gillery's bride-to-be, he had to hold his stag night on Saturday morning and rush off to the ceremony during half-time in the afternoon. Well, some of us in football still have principles and one of mine is never to refuse a drink. This is also a belief held by my squad and so, neck-high in wallop, come three o'clock we were eleven hangovers in search of a kick around. Somehow, Reg Pybus, who is such a square he even has a mono Walkman, refused to drink with the match only hours away, and so managed to get the team into their kit and out on to the pitch. I remember nothing whatever about the match, as I passed out thirty yards from the ground.

On Sunday I heard that Sidcombe have gone to the wall. This must surely mean we will not be relegated. As I told Denny d'Arcy, the Sidcombe manager, when I rang up to say good riddance, 'We are just the amoeba on the European footer lake. Clubs like ours have to try and survive on the crumbs washed from bread tossed in by the business world, to feed the mallards of the Football League.'* Still, as Sidcombe stuffed us twice this season they can go to hell. Sod solidarity!

While I was out, Reg Pybus dropped in a note saying he had been invited to Wrexham with a view to joining them as coach. Before splicing a dozen lagers, I was on

* © Les Bence 1993

the blower to Reg to tell him that hencewith and fore-forth he was no longer an employee of Athletico Whaddon. He suggested I violently introduce a turnip up my rectum because I no longer have the power to hire or fire anybody. At his own suggestion, Reg said Singh had personally removed that clause from my contract with his nail clippers. It makes me want to puke, except I did enough of that last Saturday night! Some cretins like Pybus are only in football for what they can get out of it. Well, as far as I am concerned Reg is sacked and I shall say so in the programme. No doubt when Wrexham see what a joke he is, he will be back at 'The Tip' licking a few supporters' backsides and begging for his job back.

Thank God the cricket season is almost with us. We have three more games to go before I can relax and set about re-negotiating my pitiful contracts at the club and the DSS.

I have had to stoop to pocketing the money the Supporters' Club give for raffle prizes. They gave me 25 quid this week but I rummaged through the shed and found a couple of things to stick in as prizes. In fact, the four cooking apples should have been five, but our continuing cashflow problems meant I had to disguise one of them as the reserve match ball.

ATHLETICO -WHADDON

M/SV. DIVISION 3.

TODAY

· V ·

HELLINGBORO'

£1

* OFFICIAL PROGRAMME *

	P	W	D	L	PTS
GOSLING CELTIC	31	22	5	4	71
ALBORNE	31	15	9	7	54
CLANSFORD UTD	31	16	5	10	53
SCRIMLEY ARSENAL	31	13	9	9	48
NORTHTOWN	31	14	6	11	48
HELLINGBOROUGH	31	13	8	10	47
FELTON	31	12	7	12	43
TWITCHIT ALBION	31	12	7	12	43
SPORTING HYDRA CHEMICALS	31	8	12	11	42
FRAMPTON ROVERS	31	10	10	11	40
REDLAND PARK AVENUE	31	9	13	9	40
DORNING TOWN	31	9	11	11	38
LEECH TOWN	31	9	9	13	36
CHAMDEN CITY RESERVES	31	7	11	13	32
ATH. WHADDON	31	6	2	23	20
BOTHAM WDRS	31	6	4	21	19*

* 2 points deducted.
SIDCOMBE resigned.

MANAGER'S NOTES

1st May '93

No doubt an air of sadness will pervade our match with old rivals Hellingborough today. Not only is it our last match of the season but also the last match to be played at 'The Tip'.

We go into next season, however, full of hope and with a carefree spirit. After our dour 3–0 defeat against Leech, we certainly had that carefree spirit in our midweek encounter with champions Gosling Celtic. I for one was heartened to see us just going out there and enjoying ourselves, despite going down by eight goals to one. Unfortunately, some of our supporters who had hiked to the match appeared not to have a sense of humour. With Botham Wanderers already relegated and our position safe, we will adopt this carefree attitude again today so expect to see GOALS! GOALS! GOALS!

*   *   *   *   *   *   *

Looking back over the season it seems to me supporters can have little cause for complaint. Although promotion slipped from our grasp early on, our fight for survival over the last seven months has been real nail-biting stuff. Let me assure you, I never had the slightest doubt we would stay in Division Three. As I have often said in these 'Notes', Athletico is a forward-looking club and so thoughts must now turn to next season. Already the club have appointed a new coach to replace that disgraced old stager, Reg 'Accrington Stanley' Pybus. He is Mr Anka Singh who has been in coaching for many years, running the Golden Sunset minibus hire company.

*   *   *   *   *   *   *

Our groundshare next season will show what the team is

really made of as we run out for home games on the unfamiliar battlefield of St Dodimeads Comprehensive. With the pitch being unavailable during term time, three-quarters of our games will be away. Travelling to these matches could, of course, prove expensive and some of our senior supporters may find they are unable to afford it. This could be to the club's advantage in the long-run, however, because with supporters at a loose end on Saturdays, they have an ideal opportunity to visit the 'old home' and Mr Singh's new megastore. In so doing, they will increase our chairman's profit margin and this in turn means he will be able to give me a three-figure budget with which to entice quality players.

*   *   ⁄ *   *   *   *   *

During the close season I will be contributing no less than 119 per cent of my energy to the club. My time will be spent planning new tactical strategies and introducing a far-reaching training programme which will, I am sure, inevitably lead to a complete rewriting of the Football Association's *Don Howe Coaching Manual*. On my advice, the board have determined to sweep a new broom through the club, and wheely-bin those who no longer make the grade. As a matter of fact, directly after today's game I will be going into frank discussions with the chairman to search out the real dead wood.

Looking forward to next season.

Les Bence (manager).

MULTIVITE VEGEBURGER/ SINGLETONS VALVE REPLACEMENT LEAGUE NEWS

AFC DIPLOCK held a novel celebration before the kick-off of their match against NAGGS BOTTOM CELTIC last Saturday.

'The Sidings' ground is built on the site of the old Diplock railway station which was closed in 1967. A small crowd gathered on the pitch to commemorate April 1963, when the Beatles passed through on a train to somewhere else. A number of 'We luv Paul' and 'John is fab' banners were in evidence and Diplock defender, TONY SMART, actually fainted.

*　　*　　*　　*　　*　　*　　*

Enterprising NORTHTOWN have signed Japanese international, Itsibitsi Takamoto. 'Itsi' won his cap eighteen years ago, coming on in the dying seconds of an 8–1 victory over Hong Kong. Mr Takamoto is an engineer at the Northtown Nissan plant and in his spare time enjoys building robots. Provided clearance is given by the League, Northtown manager, Norman Blick, hopes to introduce a number of them into his squad next season.

*　　*　　*　　*　　*　　*　　*

The ATHLETICO WHADDON board have instigated a new local Cup competition. With one exception, the Ken Mentle Cup is only open to school sides in the Whaddon and Mitchley area. The one exception is the Athletico first team. Whaddon boss, Les Bence, told us 'The competition might seem one-sided what with all the other teams being school sides and us also getting a bye until the semi-finals, but I am determined to see at least one cup in our cabinet this season.'

*　　　　*　　　　*　　　　*　　　　*　　　　*　　　　*

The large crowd that crammed into the new men's toilets at COLDALE TROJANS ground last month were disappointed that guests of honour, the Nolan Sisters, failed to turn up for the opening. As one wag put it, as it was the opening of the toilets, perhaps they should have invited Lou Macari.

*　　　　*　　　　*　　　　*　　　　*　　　　*　　　　*

A proposed merger between First Division HOTTON FARM COLLIERY RESERVES and their neighbours, BORUSSIA MUNCHEN URCHFONT SPORTS AND SOCIAL UNITED, has been scrapped.

Both clubs agreed that a team called Borussia Munchen Urchfont and Hotton Farm Colliery Sports and Social United Reserves was stupid.

*　　　　*　　　　*　　　　*　　　　*　　　　*　　　　*

So many fans are turning up to see Premier side CHAMDEN CITY these days that the club has been forced to buy the neighbouring supermarket. They hope to demolish the store and build a bar extension, behind the main stand, in its place.

*　　　　*　　　　*　　　　*　　　　*　　　　*　　　　*

Supporters of BOTTS COMMON CORINTHIANS will no longer have to put up with annoying cancellations or last-minute postponements because of a frost-ravaged pitch during the winter months. The club has disbanded.

*　　　　*　　　　*　　　　*　　　　*　　　　*　　　　*

HELLINGBOROUGH are holding a beer and skittles seminar next Thursday evening for budding footballers. The event will go under the title 'Dribbling for Beginners'.

*   *   *   *   *   *   *

STOP PRESS The Ken Mentle Trophy was won by Mitchley Comprehensive, who beat the Mother Theresa Convent School 3–2 in a hard-fought final.

LES IN CONFIDENCE

WEDNESDAY, 5th MAY

Pahdra Singh mounted the pavement in his Bentley this morning and pinned me to the window of the Wimpy Bar. As I struggled free he thrust an envelope into my mouth and then drove off. The note was short and to the point. 'Les, re-Athletico manager, you're sacked.'

I was still in a bewildered stupor of anger and disbelief when that Wrexham reject, Reg Pybus, called round to see me. I thought he came round to gloat and I was right. The pot-bellied tosser told me that the club wished to make a gesture in recognition of all I had done for the 'Stiffs' during my spell as manager, and after much discussion it was agreed that they could best show their appreciation by raising the price of my season ticket for next year by 25 per cent. Thanks Reg, you're a brick.

Despite bordering on acute alcoholic poisoning, somehow my sacking still hasn't sunk in. This afternoon I made what is perhaps my last visit to 'The Tip'. I stood looking at the pools of water lying on the pitch, the door of the directors' Portakabin swinging back and forth on its one remaining hinge, and I recalled the good times, remembered the bad. The wins, the defeats and more defeats. Although I am down, I still have my pride and dignity and so I thought it only right that I should remove all the silverware I had brought to the club from the trophy cabinet: my cycling proficiency medal, the Mitchley Majorettes runners-up trophy I nicked from their carnival float, my Winston Churchill commemorative coin and the photograph of Michel Platini and myself talking football outside Broadcasting

House whilst both waiting to secure Bruce Forsyth's autograph.

Still dazed and confused, I wandered over the bare earth that was once the Ken Mentle Memorial Stand. My lips quivered as I entered the small, plastic road-sweeper's hut which now acted as the home team's changing room. Familiar smells rose above the ever-present odour of the nearby sewage farm, and tears came into my eyes as my nostrils sniffed out stale liniment, old Bovril and the lingering aroma of Dave Doyle's feet.

After one last, loving look at the 'old home', I walked through the turnstiles and broke down. (For crissakes! I told the club those gates had rusted and would cause an injury, but would they bloody listen?) As I dragged myself back to the Duck and Forceps, I suddenly felt a strange empathy with the great Mike Channon. Here we both are, two footballing Doris Stokeses, two men out of time. Two stadium-sized managerial talents holding half-time team talks while the rest of the soccer world has not even kicked off yet. If the Empire State Building of English football, the FA Premier League, cannot recognise Mike's ability in management, then what hope has my talent, three blocks away on the taxi rank, where the Multivite/Singletons Division Three languishes.

Unlike Mike, however, I shall not turn my back on the game I love. I am ready and willing to take anything football can throw at me. As Brian Clough told me when I met him on the top of the Little Elm bus earlier this season — we were both going to check out Little Elm Intaflora's young Dutch forward, Kylie Van Der Graaf — 'Sadly, young man, football is like a football.' How right you were, Brian. I have certainly been kicked in the teeth by those Whaddon bastards.

Damn it! I gave my every waking hour to that club unless I was doing something else. I poured my heart, soul and a couple of vats from Nettles brewery into making it a cohesive, disciplined goal-scoring machine, only to see my dream sabotaged by soccer-illiterate shopkeepers and eleven Lego-legged, sloth-brained idiots in vaguely matching shorts. Christ! Did I not, knowing the perilous financial state of the club, refuse to take a pay rise in line with my Social Security increase?

I am not looking for, or expecting, sympathy, but as I have selflessly ridden through the valley of the Multi-vite Vegeburger/Singletons Valve Replacement League Division Three, I have taken abuse to the left of me and phlegm to the right.

I think it was John Motson who once said 'That's it. It's all over. No, it's not.' In the Hattie Jacques Cocktail Bar tonight, there are probably wry smiles on the faces of those who think they have seen the last of Leslie Bence rucking into the hurly-burly of football management. They are probably right.

Well, sod 'em.

ATHLETICO WHADDON F.C.

REQUIRE A

PLAYER/MANAGER

MANAGER

Apply; Mr P. Singh, c/o
McMenemy Villas, Whaddon